FRONTIER DOCTOR

URLING C. COE, M.D.

Thirty-five years ago the town of Farewell Bend in central Oregon was wide open and booming. Stage coaches brought pioneers, stockmen, and gamblers in ever-increasing numbers from the railroad a hundred miles away. Stores and saloons were filled with the bustle and excitement of the opening Northwest, while the primitive hotels were overflowing with transients and half the settlers were still living in tents. Beyond the limits of the town rolled a vast expanse of sage brush and stock ranches.

In all this territory no licensed physician was practicing, when young Urling Coe arrived in Bend. There was no nurse in the county, no hospital within a hundred and fifty miles. Driving a team of wild range bronchos, he covered the entire area. He delivered babies, pulled teeth, treated typhoid cases and dressed gun-shot wounds, without any trained assistant, until the railroad came to Bend in 1911 and the frontier days were over.

This is Dr. Coe's own story of his adventures, his hardships, and his buckaroo patients. He tells it with rare understanding and humor. It is the story of one of America's last frontiers.

FRONTIER DOCTOR

THE MACMILLAN COMPANY
NEW YORK · BOSTON · CHICAGO
DALLAS · ATLANTA · SAN FRANCISCO

MACMILLAN AND CO., LIMITED
LONDON · BOMBAY · CALCUTTA
MADRAS · MELBOURNE

**THE MACMILLAN COMPANY
OF CANADA, LIMITED**
TORONTO

FRONTIER DOCTOR

by URLING C. COE, M.D.

The Macmillan Company

NEW YORK 1939

CONTENTS

There's A Doctor at Farewell Bend

FIFTY miles away in the snow-clad Cascade Range, seventy-five miles deep in the pinewoods, or one hundred miles out on the desert plateau, a man falls on a rock, a tree falls on a man, a child is about to be born, or a woman lies at the door of death; and in a log hut or rough cabin a group of anxious people stand helpless. Finally one of . them breaks the silence.

"There's a doctor at Farewell Bend."

On the Deschutes River in southeastern Oregon, Farewell Bend is where the wagon-trains separated to go north and south along the Pacific Coast or westward through the mountains; and at the time of this story the wagon-trains are ancient history to the people of the plains; but it is before the day of the motor-truck; Farewell Bend is one hundred miles by four-horse stagecoach from the nearest railroad; the heavily laden freight-wagons are hauled by six- and eight-horse teams driven by artists in profanity; and the rock-walled canyons are filled with the music of the horses' bells. It is truly, as James J. Hill called it, The Last Great West.

So a husband, brother or father answers doubtfully,

"But that's a hundred miles; it's below zero; and besides, I don't know how we can ever pay him."

"The young Doc doesn't think about such things," is

the reply; and five minutes later the clatter of a running saddle-horse dies away northward.

The physician is president of a bank; and it is imperative that I see him immediately. All this particular day, save for lunch and dinner, I have waited in his office above the bank; and it is now two o'clock in a still winter night. I hear the trotting of a team of driving-ponies, the creaking of the ice beneath the buggy-wheels, and after a few minutes of silence, slow steps upon the stair and along the hall. The door opens, and the doctor enters, clad in a heavy fur coat. He nods to me, but does not speak; and instinctively, neither do I. He goes to his desk, sets his bag upon it, lays beside it a blue Colt six-shooter and a flask, opens a wall-cabinet, remembers his overcoat, removes it, serves me and himself with a glass of whiskey from the cabinet, wearily drops into a chair, and fifteen minutes later we are in the midst of our mutual business when we hear the clatter of a running saddle-horse, hurried steps upon the stair, a rap at the door, and the doctor says,

"Come in."

A man enters, closing the door with a bang by standing with his back against it, as if he were unable to stand without support. Wiping the ice from his eyebrows and unshaven face with his coat-sleeve, he peers uncertainly, first at the doctor, then at me. Physically the physician is the most powerful man I have ever known; and now, tired, dishevelled, and dirty with the stains of travel, he might have been the town blacksmith. So the visitor selected the sedentary metropolitan as the person to address, saying to me,

"My wife is dying."

The blacksmith rises, serves another glass of whiskey, and asks,

"Where is she?"

"About a hundred miles south."

The doctor dons his fur coat, fills the flask, placing it in his left pocket, the Colt in his right pocket, picks up his bag, says to me, "Handle that matter as you think right—I'll approve it," and is gone.

My acquaintance with the author of this book began where the story ends, in 1911; and this is a truthful description of our first private interview. He was still going, you see, wherever people in distress were saying, "There's a doctor at Farewell Bend."

WILLIAM DUNCAN CHENEY.

FRONTIER DOCTOR

Chapter 1

Wide-Open Town: I Arrive

WHEN I woke up that first morning in the "hotel" room, I felt pretty much pleased with myself. I was just where I wanted to be—in the heart of the last pioneer stock country of the West, ready to hang out my shingle in a wide open town. It was January tenth, 1905. I was a young medico twenty-three years old and eager to get going.

I hadn't seen the town yet. Late the night before one of those old-time frontier stage coaches had brought me to this hotel in the brand new pioneer town of Bend, which everybody called Farewell Bend, in central Oregon. It was one hundred miles to the nearest railroad station.

I slipped out of bed in the room I shared with five other men, got dressed in the freezing cold, and went to the window. Looking out I beheld a scene of such vast sparkling beauty that I was filled with surprise and delight. Near by a gay mountain river tumbled along on its way to join the mighty Columbia, far to the north. A virgin forest of Oregon pine swept away westward to the Cascade Mountains in mile after mile of unbroken verdure, clothing the rising tiers of jumbled foothills in a mantle of bright green extending far up toward the peaks.

Beyond, an endless chain of serrated mountains reared their glistening, snow-crowned summits far into the brilliant sky. It was a sublime picture.

1

I was thrilled. I hurried down to the crowded dining room for breakfast and then out to see the town and as much as I could of the majestic country surrounding it.

Bend had sprung into existence only a year before with the beginning of construction on a large irrigation project intended to reclaim thousands of acres of the sage brush and bunch grass lands of the open range for agriculture and settlement. This vast stretch of desert lay on the near side of the river, against the big pine forests on the far side; and it swept away from the town to the east and southeast for several hundred miles. The irrigation company had a number of construction camps within a short distance of town where hundreds of men were employed at high wages. The big payroll made the town.

Bend was certainly wide-open and booming, as only a new town can boom in an already rich and prosperous stock country of the West. All lines of business were already well represented but new business buildings were being rushed to completion and many new residences were under construction to accommodate the permanent people of the town. Nearly half of them were still living in tents.

Two little saw mills, one at the upper end of town run by steam and one below town run by water power from the river, were going full blast to turn out lumber for the building operations, and a brickyard was soon to be opened.

There were eight saloons with open gambling and a lusty red light district consisting of several small shacks on the river bank in the lower end of town. There was hurry and bustle on all sides with a tang of romance and excitement in the air. The hotel was overflowing with new guests continually arriving, and the stores, saloons, and streets were full of busy, excited people.

Freighters, stockmen, buckaroos, sheep herders, timber cruisers, gamblers, and transients of all kinds who had been attracted to the town by the boom, thronged the bars or played at the gambling games, and the stores were doing a rushing business. The stores remained open in the evenings and the saloons stayed open all night and all day Sunday, and many of the laborers from the construction camps spent the week ends in town, drinking, gambling, carousing, or fighting.

Every stage that came the hundred miles from the end of the railroad was loaded with new settlers. Big freight wagons, usually with a trailer or two hooked on behind and drawn by ten to sixteen horses, brought tons of freight of all kinds into town and went back to the railroad loaded with hides, pelts, and wool from the big stock ranches in the interior.

In addition to the railroad freight charges, merchants had to pay three cents a pound and sometimes more to have their merchandise hauled in from the end of the railroad. That made it very costly, but everyone seemed to have plenty of money and spent it freely.

Exciting rumors heard on all sides were to the effect that the Hill and Harriman Lines would soon start building railroads into Bend to tap the timber of the largest virgin pine forest in the United States. Real estate men and timber locators were doing a brisk business, while the prices of city property, irrigated and farm lands, and timber, were soaring steadily upward.

Stretching away for hundreds of miles to the east and

southeast from the town was a vast expanse of semi-arid, rolling plateau country, covered with sage brush, bunch grass, and occasional small patches of scrubby juniper trees, and dotted here and there with large stock ranches. This vast unfenced area constituted the great stock ranges of eastern Oregon, southern Idaho, northern Nevada, and northeastern California. It was the largest area in the United States without a railroad, and the last frontier of the thrilling and romantic Old West. It was the home of the jack rabbit, the coyote, the badger, the bob cat, the sage hen, the big mule deer and the fleet and graceful prong-horned antelope. Here, also, thousands upon thousands of wild range horses, cattle and sheep grazed on the open range the year around.

In the forest country across the river big game of all kinds was plentiful, and the clear mountain lakes and sparkling streams swarmed with many varieties of gamey trout.

When I first came to town I started a diary in which I planned to record the important events of my first year of practice. I was soon much too busy to keep it up. But I noted my arrival in Bend on the tenth. A black bear visited town by swimming the Deschutes River on the thirteenth. Two huge mountain lions visited town, one on the twelfth, the other on the fifteenth. On the sixteenth a rancher rode in with a lion tied on the back of his saddle. It was only a moderately sized lion, but measured seven feet from nose to tail.

I was interested and amazed in the stories I heard and articles I read of the doings of the "Crook County Sheep Shooters Association," an organization of cattle men sworn to drive all sheep men out of the country and keep any new ones from coming in. Here is a clipping I saved at the time:

"On the evening of February 3, 1904, five masked riders visited a corral in the Christmas Lake Country in which a flock of 3000 sheep owned by the Benham Brothers had been placed. A sack was placed over the head of the herder and he was forced to stand under a tree. With rifle, pistols, knives, and clubs, the masked men started the slaughter at dusk, and continued the work most of the night. The sheep stampeded and about 500 escaped, only to fall prey to the coyotes. The herder was warned, and then turned loose. The sheep killers were never found but J. C. Conn of Silver Lake, who was believed to know who the masked riders were, was later found dead in a field with several bullets in his body."

I was soon to learn a great many more things about life on the range.

I was enthusiastic over the new country I had chosen to locate in, optimistic for the future of the new town, and eager to open up my office and get started. There was no vacant space suitable for an office in the overcrowded, booming town; but I was assured I'd be fixed up in a few days. A second story was being added to the little frame building at the end of the principal business street that housed the town's only bank. I secured two rooms on the second floor and waited, impatiently, for them to be completed.

Adjoining my offices was the central office of the local telephone company. In other words, "Central" was at my right hand, a very great convenience. She was a gray-haired, Victorian maiden lady, oddly at home in this Wild

West boom town; an admirable woman as well as an obliging and efficient operator.

There were two other doctors in the town, but they had no license to practice in Oregon and departed soon after I opened my office. A third doctor, an old retired physician from the Middle West, ran the only drug store in town. He did not want to practice and would take a case only in emergencies when no other doctor was available.

To the north it was ninety miles to the nearest doctor. On the west it was a hundred and twenty miles. To the south it was ninety-four miles. In the county seat, Prineville, thirty-five miles to the east, there were four doctors who had ranged the enormous territory, as large as some New England states, but with only thirty-six hundred people, about half of whom lived in Prineville, in 1900, before our town of Bend came into existence.

There was not a graduate nurse in the county, and the nearest hospital was a hundred and sixty miles away.

By the time my offices were ready, I had started to size up the situation. I moved in my trunk, filled with books and instruments, as the carpenters moved out. There was no light or water system in the town. For heating the office I secured a large wood-burning stove; and I bought a big kerosene lamp to light each room. I engaged a carpenter to put up some shelves in one corner of the operating room and make a box lounge for the reception room. I bought three chairs, a rough pine table, a water bucket and dipper. I sent to Portland for a metal operating table. As soon as the linoleum was laid and I had carried a bucket of water from the river a block and a half away, I was all set and ready for business.

I didn't have to wait long.

CHAPTER 2

Doctor to Buckaroos

I HAD always wanted to be a doctor like my father before me. The story goes that I came into the house one day when I was about six and announced that when I grew up I was going to be a big fat doctor. Mother just shook her head. She knew only too well the wearisome toil, the long hours with broken sleep, the heavy responsibilities, and the sheafs of unpaid bills that play so large a part in a doctor's life. Father knew these things, too; he never encouraged me or discouraged me.

We lived in Carthage, Missouri, down in the southwestern part of the state, where my father practiced medicine and I grew up. I studied medicine at the University of Missouri where I played football, baseball and the clarinet. Later I went to the Eclectic Medical College of Cincinnati, where my father had gone, graduating with top honors.

As a youngster, much of my idle time was spent around my father's office and I often rode out with him on his calls. Many times when I was free from school he took me along to drive for him so that he could get in a little sleep, a commodity of which he was always running short, what with long distances and night calls. One day when I was thirteen and we were alone in the office, I told Father that I had fully made up my mind to be a doctor

7

regardless of Mother's opposition. He listened to what I had to say in grave silence, eyeing me thoughtfully over his glasses.

"All right. I'll take you along with me to-morrow," he said.

So the next morning I drove him to the home of an old gentleman I knew well whom I had always seen wearing a long white beard. When I saw him with his beard shaved off and a big, repulsive looking epithelioma (cancer) protruding from his lower lip, I admit I was shocked. While another doctor administered the anaesthetic my father removed the cancer and the entire lower lip with it. The sight of the old gentleman's mutilated face, covered with blood, exposing a few old snags of teeth, gurgling and bubbling as he breathed, was not a pretty one. I must have behaved well, however, for Father seemed satisfied. It may be he was trying to test me.

The very next day he took me with him when he went to amputate the leg of one of his fellow doctors who had fallen under the wheels of a moving train. I helped steady the leg while he sawed the bone.

A short time after that Father took me ten miles into the country to drive for him, being badly in need of the doze he could get in the buggy on the way. When we arrived at the farmhouse we found that the farmer had a strangulated hernia (a rupture with abdominal contents protruding through an opening in the abdominal wall that could not be replaced).

An immediate operation was required and there was no other doctor available to give the anaesthetic. So I was pressed into service. The operation went smoothly and I was thrilled and delighted. By now I began to think I was well on the way to becoming a doctor myself. From that day on it was settled. Mother's opposition subsided and finally ceased.

After I graduated, I took a course in Psychology and Suggestive Therapeutics under Dr. Geo. F. Pitzer, a leading psychologist at that time. Meanwhile our family had moved to San Francisco where Father had built up a lucrative practice, and I went in with him. By now his practice was nearly all office and hospital work, and it was too tame for me. The hours were long and the duties confining. I have always disliked living in cities—the farther I can get away from civilization the better I like it. I finally told Father I could not stand the confinement and monotony, that I wanted to go out on my own. Father understood and let me go.

I started looking around and arrived in Portland, where by sheer chance I ran into a young medic who was wearing the same medical college fraternity pin that I was. We gave each other the high sign and struck up an acquaintance. He was planning to take the examination before the State Board of Medical Examiners for Oregon. I thought that might be a good idea for myself. I took the examination, passed with flying colors, landed in the new town of Bond, the spot I selected for myself—a brand new country with plenty of hunting, fishing, mountain and desert and forest and wide-open boom town excitements, plenty of adventure.

I found adventure, but precious little time for hunting or fishing or the delights of a wide-open town. I was the Doc and, as we all know, doctors are not supposed to be human—at any rate in their professional capacities.

After I was established in my crude offices, I sat down and waited for patients. Within three days I was fairly busy. I was called up out of bed two or three nights a week to patch up some unlucky fellow who had been in a fight in one of the saloons or gambling houses.

Then came my first call outside town. Seven miles down the river was the little town of Laidlaw—a general store which harbored the only telephone, a "hotel," a blacksmith shop, a few scattered houses.

A buckaroo rode up in front of the store one day and asked the storekeeper to telephone for a doctor for a sick man in a little town seventeen miles farther down the river. He then rode away without giving the storekeeper further information. The storekeeper called Miss Hastings, the telephone operator, and she gave me the message.

With a spirited team of broncos from the livery stable, I drove down to the town, where the supposed sick man was, in a little more than two hours. Upon my arrival I found the man was not sick but injured. His right foot was crushed and almost severed from the leg at the ankle, but was still hanging by the large tendon of the heel and a few strips of mangled flesh and skin.

He had been hauling lumber with a four-horse team, wagon, and trailer, and in trying to negotiate a sharp hair-pin turn on a grade cut out of the hillside, the trailer had slipped over the edge of the grade and turned over, taking the wagon with it. His foot was caught between the load and the rocks on the hillside. His partner, who had been following on another load, had tied a length of rope tightly around the leg below the knee to control the bleeding, and the leg below the rope, where the circulation had been shut off, was very sodden and badly swollen. He was then taken to the general store in town.

I saw at once that if the circulation was kept out of the leg much longer it would have to be amputated above the knee. Thinking I was going to see a sick man I had taken with me only my medicine case full of drugs instead of my surgical equipment. I had no surgical dressings and no instruments except those in a little pocket case such as were carried in the hip pocket by doctors in those days. It contained two small scalpels, artery forceps, scissors, needles, and some sutures; but nothing with which to cut off the jagged ends of the protruding bones. If I went back to Bend for my instruments or sent some one else the round trip of forty-eight miles would require four or five hours and the patient would have to lose more of his leg. I was in an awkward and embarrassing predicament. I thought my future was ruined.

Feeling very chagrined and foolish, I explained the situation to the men who had gathered around the patient in the store.

They listened in grave silence while I offered all the excuses I could think of for my blunder, and I imagined there was a bit of scorn in the looks they gave me. At that point, the storekeeper suddenly remembered he had a butcher's saw somewhere in a shipment of goods that were still unpacked: he asked if it would do to saw the bones with. I hastened to tell him it would and felt greatly relieved. Luckily I had enough chloroform for an anaesthetic.

The storekeeper's wife donated a bed sheet, which was torn into strips and sterilized for dressings. The butchers' saw was found and sterilized along with the instruments in the pocket case by boiling in a wash boiler on the kitchen stove.

By that time several more men had gathered in the store but no one among them had ever seen an anaesthetic given. One of them consented to give the chloroform, under my supervision, however, and the foot was quickly amputated without trouble. An unused counter in the back of the store served as an operating table, and the men stood by and watched the operation.

I felt greatly relieved when it was finished but soon began to wonder if the wound would be infected, and worried about it all the way home. I slept little that night because of the worry about the possibility of infection, and drove down to dress the stump early the next morning. The following day the patient was brought to town in a wagon so I could see him every day.

That case served as a good object lesson to me and I immediately arranged my equipment so that I would not blunder again and go to the country unprepared. I had a medicine case which contained fifty-four different drugs of an assortment sufficient for any case of sickness. An obstetrical bag was stocked with everything required in a confinement case. A large canvas telescope was filled with plaster bandages, splints, gauze bandages, and everything needed in a fracture case. Another bag held an amputating outfit and all the instruments needed for an operation of any kind. In addition to these I equipped an emergency bag with anaesthetics, antiseptics, soap, sterile towels and dressings; a series of enameled basins of graduated sizes that fitted one into the other; and everything needed in an emergency not provided for in the other bags. When I went to the country in the buggy I always took all five bags and was then thoroughly equipped.

A few days after the teamster had his foot crushed there was an explosion in one of the construction camps that injured two men.

One man was sitting on a ledge of rock holding a hand drill for his partner to strike with a sledge to drill a hole for blasting. They unknowingly drilled into an old undischarged shot of dynamite which exploded.

The man who held the drill had the little finger of his left hand blown off, and his face, neck, and body filled with small particles of rock and fine gravel, embedded just under the skin, as though he had been shot with a gun loaded with gravel.

The Swede who had been striking the drill had the upper part of his body and face shot full of fine rock and gravel and a deep gash cut in his face. He had been struck with the sharp, knife-like edge of a wedge-shaped rock that laid his face open from the inner corner of his right eye down diagonally through his nose to the left side of the mouth. Several teeth were knocked out and the hard palate was split to the depth of about an inch. Both men had their eyes filled with sand and dust and completely closed.

It was impossible for the Swede to take an anaesthetic of any kind by inhalation and allow room for me to work on the big gash in his face. He was given a hypodermic of hyoscine, morphine, and cactine, and I went to work on him as soon as it had taken effect. It was a tedious job to remove all the dirt and gravel from the wound in his face, and it required a good many stitches to close the big gash, but he did not flinch or make the slightest complaint.

The other man's injuries were much less severe than those of the Swede, and he was given the same kind of a hypodermic, but he made a terrible fuss when I dressed his wounds. Some of the men of the camp standing in the tent watching the dressing, laughed at him because of his lack of nerve until he became so offended and disgruntled that he shut up and ceased to complain. He was a tender-foot who had been in the country only a few weeks.

The men who lived the hard life of the frontier, shared the Indian's belief that it was cowardly to flinch from pain. They considered anyone a sissy who would ask for an anaesthetic to have a few stitches taken or a fracture reduced.

The day following the explosion in the camp the third accident came. A man who was sawing shingles in a little sawmill ten miles from town had his right hand caught in the saw. While the doctor who ran the drug store administered the anaesthetic, I amputated the mutilated remains of all four fingers and thumb, leaving stumps the length of one finger joint. His case completed the first series of three accident cases, and there were no more for a time.

For some inexplicable reason accident cases always came in groups or series of three. Whenever I had an accident case I was always sure of having two more within a short time. As soon as the first accident case was cared for I always looked over and restocked my emergency bag to be ready for the next two cases that were sure to follow within a few days. When the third case had been taken care of an interval of days, or more likely weeks, would elapse before the next series occurred.

The injuries of the two men who were blown up in the

construction camp were dressed in a tent there on the desert, with the sand and dust blowing around under foot, a thick layer of dust covering everything in the tent; but there was no sign of infection in either case. The marked absence of infection in that country was always a marvel to me and I never ceased to wonder at it. As a rule, wounds that were not even properly dressed in the beginning did not become infected. It was probably owing to the fact that the air was so pure and dry, and there was so much sunshine—320 full days of sunshine a year.

The construction work on the irrigation canals, much of which was rock work involving dynamiting, on which five or six hundred men were employed (with an additional 500 in a flux of going between the camps and the town on sprees or sobering up) made Sunday a busy day for me.

One Sunday afternoon while I was busy in the private room patching up the battered head and cut face of an hombre who had been mixed up in a fight, I heard unsteady footsteps come down the hallway; they entered my reception room where several people were waiting.

"Where's Doc?" I heard.

Somebody said I was busy in the other room. A man popped his head in—

"Say, Doc, I want a physic," he bawled.

"All right," I said, "just sit down and wait your turn. I'll be with you in a minute."

He was quiet for a bit, then opened the door again and bellowed as before, "Doc, I want a physic."

After he had kept this thing up a while, I got exasperated and was just going to throw him out when I suddenly decided that a better plan would be to give him his physic and get rid of him.

Among the drugs I had been able to get for my office was some powdered podophyllum (mandrake root) which in doses of one fourth of a grain is a certain and powerful cathartic, although it requires six or eight hours to act. I hurriedly poured out enough to make two powders, which I estimated contained about two grains each, folded them in powder papers, and gave them to the drunk. I told him to take one and if that didn't work in two or three hours to take the second. He left the office and I forgot all about him. A few Sundays later I met him on the street very happily drunk but did not recognize him until he spoke.

"Say, Doc, did I ever pay you for that physic you give me in the office that day?" he inquired.

"No, you did not," I replied.

"No, and by God I never will. That was the damm'est stuff I ever see. Any time I want a physic now all I got to do is go look at that there little paper the damn stuff was wrapped in, and it turns me inside out."

I never asked him to pay for it.

One of the cases of those first few days was that of John J . . . . from South Ca'lina. John was about forty, of medium height and powerful, stocky build with a thick chest and heavy shoulders. With his blue-black hair and mustache and piercing black eyes, he was rather good looking. He was well nourished and the picture of health.

John said he had been "ailin' fer about fifteen or sixteen years" and that no doctor had yet been able to help him. He said he felt "jest no account nohow and not able to work." But although he did not work, he did a lot of fishing and hunting, while his wife made the living by taking in washing and chamber work at the hotel. He and his wife had filed on timber claims and a homestead of a hundred and sixty acres. In five years they would be able to sell their joint holdings for fifteen or sixteen thousand dollars. John was the master of his house and occasionally beat his wife within moderate and considerate limits.

He recited a long list of aches, pains and symptoms, some of which I had never heard of before; but he said he was sure I could find out what was wrong with him and cure him of "ailin'." I was not rushed that day and spent half the afternoon examining and questioning him. When I was through I knew no more than when I started, and as he was apparently sound I had a strong suspicion that his principal ailment was just plain laziness. I withheld making a diagnosis and had him return the next day. I puzzled over his case all night and the next day took a sample of blood and sent it to the nearest laboratory, 260 miles away in Portland. A week or ten days later the laboratory report came and I summoned John to the office.

"How do you feel today, John?"

"Well I feel—I feel—a—I guess I feel kin'ly, kin'ly, kin'ly weak."

"John, did you ever have a sore, or an ulcer that would not heal readily?"

"Yes, I did one time."

"How long ago was that?"

"Well that was 'bout fifteen or sixteen yar ago, I reckon."

"Now I'll tell you what's the matter with you, John. You've got syphilis. The laboratory report of your Wassermann test was four plus positive."

"Syphilis? What's that thar—do you mean I got the old rall?" he asked with deep concern.

"Yes, that's it," I said. John stared at the floor in silence and deep concern for a few minutes and then said, half to himself:

"I jes' kaint onderstan' it." Whereupon I explained as fully and carefully as I could what the disease was and what it might mean to him. But John just sat there staring at the floor and scratching his head thoughtfully.

"I kaint onderstan' it."

"What is it you can't understand about it, John?" I asked.

"Why! How come I ta git this here dose?"

"You got it from some woman," I assured him.

"Oh, shoo, shoo, I know all that. But do you know that thar woman was tha most religiousest woman I ever seed in all my born days, an' more'n that it was to camp meetin' where I got it. I kaint onderstan' it."

After treatment John improved and got over feeling kin'ly weak, even took to doing a little work on rare occasions. But he continued to spend most of his time fishing and hunting, and it took a mighty good man to keep up with him in the mountains.

It was just nine days after the office was opened that I was called to the first case of serious sickness I treated. The proprietor of the hotel where I stayed called me to attend his cook, Charlie Grant, after he had put Grant to bed in a loft over the butcher shop across the street from the hotel.

I found Charlie sitting on the side of his bed half-dressed. His face was pale and pinched; his eyes were glassy and staring; his head and neck were covered with great beads of sweat while tears ran down his cheeks. He gasped for breath and moaned with pain, holding his right side. He had lobar pneumonia.

The butcher's family lived in rooms in the building on the ground floor, in the rear of the shop. The second story was one large unfinished room, or loft, probably thirty by seventy feet in dimensions, unceiled inside and covered with a shingle roof. An outside stairway led up to a landing at the second floor level, where a door gave entrance to the loft at the rear. At the front of the loft farthest from the door, rough pine board partitions about seven feet high had been erected, to form four rooms of about ten by twelve feet. Each of these rooms held a double bed, for overflow guests from the hotel, where they slept two in a bed, regardless of previous acquaintance, and paid two dollars and a half each, per night. The remainder of the big loft was all in one large room called "the bull pen." It was filled to capacity every night with laborers, freighters, buckaroos, sheep herders, timber cruisers and the like, who carried their own roll of bedding and paid one dollar each per night for the privilege of spreading their blankets on the floor. There was no heat or plumbing in the loft.

Grant being such an important personage as a cook, as well as a sick man, was given a whole bed and room to himself. There were no doors to the partitioned-off rooms but a blanket was hung over the opening to serve as a door to Grant's room.

This Charlie Grant, a man of fifty, had run away from his home in the East, when a lad in his teens, to seek his fortune in the wild and woolly West, and had drifted from place to place all along the frontiers, from Canada to Mexico. His career had been extremely varied, but he had spent most of his time and talents in breaking wild horses, dealing poker and faro bank in gambling houses, and cooking. While cooking on a large stock ranch he had heard of the new town of Bend, and thinking that better opportunities awaited him there, or that he would at least be nearer to an unfailing supply of liquor—to Charlie the elixir of life—he came to the new town.

Good white cooks were usually scarce, most of the cooks along the frontier being Chinese, and Charlie at once secured the position of chief cook at the hotel.

For three months he had slaved in the hot kitchen without relaxation, doing his work to the entire satisfaction of the hotel proprietor, although he consumed a quart of whiskey regularly every day. In seeking relaxation at the end of his work one evening, he wandered around the saloons and got into a poker game, where he won a fair sized stake. Being so favored by Lady Luck would prompt most any man to honor the fickle lady in some manner and for a man of Charlie's proclivities it called for a grand celebration of the convivial variety, with gay and protracted wassail.

He went on a spree with some newly found friends until he was drunk enough to imagine he could beat the roulette wheel, and he continued to "buck the tiger" until he lost his last gold eagle on the double 0. Then he retired to his tent on the river bank and lay down on his bed without undressing to sleep off the effects of his grand celebration. The night was bitter cold and he awoke in the morning with a heavy cold, a splitting headache, and a severe pain in his side. Realizing that both his stomach and pockets were empty, he dragged himself back to the kitchen, but was too sick to work and soon collapsed. The hotel proprietor was glad to see him back, after having been without a cook for three days, and thought he would be able to work as soon as he had time to get sober, so he gave him the bed in the loft and called me.

With the severest type of lobar pneumonia, he was a very sick man who needed constant treatment and the best of care. The loft was a wretched place for him in the bitter cold weather, but the nearest hospital was a hundred and sixty miles away, and there was not a professional nurse in the county. Grant was among strangers and without money or friends. The hotel proprietor was furnishing him with bed and board. It seemed to be up to me to do the rest.

His fever was so high that he was soon irrational and delirious and could not be left alone a minute or he would try to get out of bed. I had to get some one to stay with him at all times and act as nurse, but it seemed impossible to find a man who did not have steady work. After much canvassing I finally found a tall, quiet, soft voiced, young cow-boy from Texas, who agreed to stay with him from six in the morning until six in the evening for five dollars a shift and board. Five dollars a day was the minimum wage for common labor in Bend at that time.

I had still more trouble in finding a night nurse but finally found a tin horn gambler who had lost his bankroll to take the night shift at five dollars a night. He called himself "The Dead Game Sport, from Bowling Green, Kentucky." I did not like his looks or disposition, but he was the only man who would take the job.

Both nurses ate at the hotel and carried whatever food that was suitable for the sick man over to him: but there was little that was suitable for him on the hotel menu. There were no chickens raised near town, and no eggs to be had at any price. There were many large cattle ranches with thousands of heads of cattle, but there were no milk cows among them. The only milk procurable was the condensed variety in cans. There were no fruit juices obtainable; to secure proper nourishment for the sick man was a problem.

Keeping him warm was another difficulty. For three successive nights the outdoor temperature ranged from seventeen to nineteen degrees below zero. A bucket of water setting by the head of the sick man's bed on the third night had become a solid mass of ice by morning. The loft was a noisy place with fifty or sixty men snoring in every variety of tone, from the highest pitched falsetto to the deepest bass. The noise resembled a conglomeration of steam calliopes, bull frogs, katydids, tin whistles, and coyotes, all singing in a different key and each one clamoring for supremacy. While the main chorus snored others were coming and going at all hours.

"What kind of a damn menagerie have they got out there?" Grant asked, during one of his rational moments.

After the first day his delirium became constant. With all the hubbub and commotion going on all night in the "bull pen," Grant lay there raving continually with a wild and fantastic delirium, in spite of extremely heavy doses of sedatives, while the "Dead Game Sport from Bowling Green" walked the floor with his overcoat on to keep warm. I fully expected that the combination of alcoholism and pneumonia would be fatal, as I had been taught in medical college that alcoholics rarely survive pneumonia, but I pitched into the case with the determination to win if possible.

The gambler brought his midnight lunch in a tin dinner pail each evening, and took along a bottle of whiskey to keep him warm during the cold night.

Just before daylight on the third morning a man who had been sleeping in the "bull pen" came to the hotel and wakened me. The gambler nurse was drunk and careless and had been abusive to the patient during the night. I went over to the loft immediately and found the drunken gambler sound asleep in a chair by the bed. I was furious.

Without saying a word I seized the "Dead Game Sport" by the coat collar, dragged him out onto the landing at the head of the stairs, and gave him a good swift kick that sent him skidding down the stairs into a pile of snow at the bottom. I then went back and stayed with the sick man until the Texas cow-boy nurse came at six o'clock.

While I was eating supper in the hotel that evening, a bartender from a saloon a block away came and called me out of the dining room to warn me that the gambler had sworn to "get me" that night when I made my regular visit to Grant. He had been loafing in the saloon all afternoon nursing his grudge at me for throwing him out, fortifying his courage with numerous drinks.

"That hombre's a bad man, Doc," the bartender warned. "He's got a mighty bad reputation up around Butte, where he come from, an' he's packin' a wicked lookin' knife ta stab ya with. Are ya heeled, Doc?" he asked. "If ya ain't, I'd be glad to let ya take my gun ta plug the dirty bastard with."

Whereupon he pulled a big .45 Colt six-shooter out of

his overcoat pocket and offered it to me. I thanked him for the tip and the offer of the gun, but told him I would not need it. He looked at me dubiously, as much as to say, "Well, all right, if you don't want it—but if anything happens and you're not heeled, don't blame me."

I had a good gun of my own, but it was too big to carry conveniently without a belt and holster, and I did not want the gambler to see me toting a gun to make him think I was afraid of him.

After finishing supper, I went over to see Grant much earlier than usual.

From a pile of waste lumber under the stairway of the building I selected a piece of pine two-by-four, two or three feet long. I whittled one end of it down to a convenient size to be grasped in the hand easily and put it in the corner behind the door.

After finishing my attentions to Grant, I took my position behind the door and waited. At last I heard footsteps coming stealthily up the stairs and stop on the landing outside the door.

I was sure it was the "Dead Game Sport." I stood quietly inside the door listening, but heard nothing more for a moment but the pounding of my own heart. In a moment the door opened an inch or two and he peeped cautiously inside. I was back in the corner in the dark where he did not see me. Then the door opened a little wider and he stuck his head inside but did not see me—he was looking in the other direction. I was tempted to take a whack at his head but waited, while my heart pounded and my nerves were tense. Then he opened the door cautiously and stepped inside. I came out from behind the door quickly with my club raised and swinging at his head, but he saw me in time to sidestep and duck.

"D—D—D-Don't hit me fer Chrisesake Doc! I—I-I wasn't goin' ta start nothin'," he stammered. "I jest come to git ma dinner pail. Gim'me ma dinner pail an' I won't bother ya no more."

"Well get down out of here and stay out, and I'll throw your pail down after you," I said.

I found his dinner pail where he had left it by the head of the bed and tossed it down to him at the foot of the stairs. I then went back to the sick man and saw no more of the gambler that night.

The following day my friend the bartender asked me what happened when the "Dead Game Sport" entered the loft, so I told him about it. He then told me he had feared trouble and had followed the gambler to the building. He had stayed out of sight and hid under the stairs after the gambler went up. He heard the gambler come down after a few minutes and peeped out at him when he picked up his dinner pail. Then he saw him take his bowie knife out of his coat sleeve and put it away in its sheath under his arm, where he always carried it. I never heard of any more threats from the "Dead Game Sport."

In the beginning I did not think Grant would live more than a week. Considering his abominable surroundings in the big, cold, noisy loft, the lack of proper nourishment, the fact that his attendants knew nothing of nursing, except for horses and cattle, and the fact that he had been a heavy drinker—all these factors left his prospects for recovery pretty slight.

I spent all my spare time at his bedside and did everything I could possibly do for him. The night he passed the crisis I stayed with him all night long and gave him burnt brandy and stimulants until his pulse was stronger.

It was a mighty close call for the old boy but his amazing vitality pulled him through, though if I had not given him the attention I did the result would have been different. He slowly but steadily improved after he passed the crisis, but he did not get out of the loft until the last of May.

When he finally was able to get up and around, he seemed grateful and told everybody I had saved his life. I had also paid his expenses out of my own pocket because he was broke and among strangers—maybe, partly, because he was my first serious patient.

After he was able to work he earned some money breaking horses but did not offer to pay me. Then he went to another town and started a lunch counter which prospered and grew into a restaurant. I wrote him asking him to pay me the amount I had spent, enclosing, also, a bill for my services. No reply. I sent the bill to a collector.

It seems that when the restaurant was making money, Grant went back to his old pleasures, gambling and drinking to excess. He lost everything and left town, flat broke. At any rate, the bill was uncollectable.

I was surprised but more disappointed. That was a shock to the young doctor. It makes me smile now. When people are sick they think the doctor is a pretty good fellow, entitled to some payment for his work and worry. But after they are well again, they begin to wonder if the Doc did so much for them after all. And when the bill comes in they shed their gratitude as naturally as a buck deer sheds his horns.

CHAPTER 3

Wild West Babies

I WAS called to my first confinement on the third night after the office was opened. It was not only my first baby case; it was the first delivery at which I had ever been present. I was apprehensive for fear I might blunder or make some mistake, but Lady Luck was very kind and gave me an easy normal birth to start me off.

It was the second child of a young woman who had had a very hard labor with her first baby, and since this second one was so easy, she and her family thought I must be a wonderful obstetrician.

She had had no anaesthetic with the first baby, but at my suggestion took chloroform with the second and thereafter raved about it. The news that she had taken chloroform spread over the community rapidly. Many of the older women condemned her for taking it. They believed it contrary to divine decree. The matter was as widely discussed as though it had been an important new scientific discovery.

Some had a general fear of all anaesthesia; some feared it might be detrimental to the baby; and others thought it forbidden by the Bible. Most of the old pioneers considered it cowardly to want an anaesthetic to ease labor pains, and considered those of the younger generation who did so to be weaklings, inferior to the women of their own generation. I always began giving my patients chloroform when their pains became severe in the second stage of labor, and never yet knew a woman to take a few whiffs without asking for more. It was not long before there was a complete change in the attitude toward anaesthetics in labor, and nearly every woman not only expected one but asked for it when the proper time came.

The first confinement case demonstrated to me that my didactic training in obstetrics had been adequate. That gave me confidence for the host of baby cases that came thick and fast thereafter. The cold frosty nights of the higher altitudes were detrimental to some of the more tender farm crops, but they were evidently conducive to a large baby crop, for the country had about the highest birth rate and the lowest death rate of any section of the United States.

There were many nights when I delivered two babies and sometimes three; and I distinctly remember one night when I was in attendance on four women in labor at the same time, all in different houses in town; and all four babies were born within a nine-hour period.

When I started to practice, it was not generally known in that country that every pregnant woman should be under the care of a doctor during the full term of her pregnancy, and few of them consulted me until I was called to deliver them after labor had already started. Most people seemed to think that a pregnant woman was obliged to endure a certain amount of nausea, vomiting, and other unpleasant symptoms, and never thought of consulting a doctor unless their symptoms were unusually severe. When I became aware of this situation I began an educational campaign to get all expectant mothers to consult me as soon as they knew they were pregnant.

Many of the women among the older settlers, especially those who lived far from town, did not even have a doctor for all their confinements but often depended on some neighbor woman with a little midwifery experience to take care of them. Fortunately, puerperal infection (infection of the mother at the time of childbirth) was practically unknown in that country, and the midwives got along fairly well in normal cases.

In some of the cases far out in the country I was alone with the mother when the baby came, the husband having gone after some neighbor woman, who might live anywhere from five to fifteen miles away, to come and act as nurse. In such cases I managed the delivery alone, washed and dressed the baby, and sometimes cooked breakfast for the mother and myself while waiting for the husband and neighbor nurse to arrive.

In some of these cases I was obliged to make a forceps delivery alone. I had a special harness constructed, my own invention, for use in such cases. It had large leather cuffs to go around the thighs with an adjustable metal bar between them to hold the thighs wide apart. From the thigh cuffs a leather strap ran up over the shoulders and held the knees up to the chest with the thighs flexed on the abdomen.

The anaesthetic was managed by firmly packing a large wad of cotton in the bottom of an ordinary drinking glass so tightly that it would not fall out when the glass was inverted. The cotton was saturated with chloroform and given to the patient to hold in her own hand. She was then told to hold the inverted glass over her nose and inhale regularly and fairly deeply. When she had taken enough chloroform to make her insensible to pain and put her to sleep, her hand relaxed and she dropped the glass before she took too much.

In the meantime I went ahead with the instrumental delivery until the effect of the chloroform began to wear off and the patient began to wake up. Then she was told to pick up the glass and inhale more of the chloroform, while I resumed the operation. In that way I was able to make successful forceps deliveries without help. But to manage a delivery of that sort in a little cramped shack on the desert was hard work that demanded both skill and ingenuity.

With the coming of spring the confinement cases increased in number.

Tired out and much in need of sleep, I had gone to bed early one night in my room in the hotel when I heard a horse come into town on a dead run and pass on down the street toward the livery stable. I knew instinctively that some one was after me for some urgent case and was instantly wide awake.

In a few minutes I heard the heavy footfalls of high-heeled boots and jingling spurs come stomping up the hotel stairs and down the hallway toward my room.

"Oh Doc, where ya at?" a voice shouted.

I jumped out of bed, opened the door, and saw an excited young buckaroo of sixteen or seventeen standing in the hall. His big blue eyes were bulging from a youthful face that was pale and pinched, where it was not covered with a generous coating of dirt and clotted blood, and he was covered with sand and dust from head to heels. He

limped into the room holding his right arm flexed across
the front of his body, supported by his left hand.

"What's the trouble?" I asked.

"I was comin' after you, Doc, a ridin' ta beat hell
through the sage brush in the dark, an' that goddam onry
hunk o' buzzard meat o' Sid Powers's I was ridin' went an'
hit a badger hole an' fell, an' throwed me plumb over his
head fer 'bout twenty feet. It like ta knocked me plumb
silly, an' fer a spell I didn't know where in the hell I was
at. It made tha damn cayuse a little bit lame, but I'm a
damn sight worse stove up than he is right now."

"Where did you come from?" I asked.

"I'm the wrangler fer tha remuda out to Sid Powers's
camp 'bout thirty mile out here on tha desert where
we're ridin' fer hosses. But I wasn't comin' after ye fer
myself—it's Sid Powers's wife. She's layin' out yonder in
tha camp on tha desert an' I reckon she's mighty bad
hurt."

"What happened to her?" I asked, as I slid into my
clothes.

"She got throwed," he replied, "an' it come damn near
killin' her, but the worst part of it is she's jest 'bout due ta
have a baby. Sid 's mighty bad skeered 'bout her an' he
wants ya to git out there jest as quick as ever ye kin. He
give me tha best fresh hoss there was in tha remuda an'
told me ta haze hell outen 'im all tha way in here an' not
to pay no 'tention to hurtin' tha hoss, but ta git ye out
there jest as quick as ever I could. I was makin' mighty
good time an' was aimin' ta have jest enough hoss left ta
git to tha barn with when I got in here, but tha damn bastard went an' hit that badger hole."

The right side of the horse-wrangler's head, face, and

body were covered with bruises and abrasions, and his right shoulder was dislocated. He was evidently suffering a good deal of pain, but his concern for the injured woman and the excitement of the hard ride had kept him going. He had nerve to continue his ride in the condition he was in after the hard fall; for running fast over the desert with the horse jumping and dodging the clumps of sage brush is no rocking-chair ride.

I gave him a hypodermic of morphine, reduced the dislocation of his shoulder, and dressed the worst of his cuts and abrasions, while a team and buggy was being hitched for me at the livery stable. When we went to the livery stable for the team I saw the poor horse the wrangler had ridden and felt as much sympathy for it as I did for the rider. It had been a fine horse before that thirty mile race with time, but now it was very lame in the shoulder and had great welts on its sides from the quirt.

The young buckaroo left his horse there and went with me as guide to the camp, which was on the open desert ten miles from the road. As we drove rapidly out the road he told me the story of the accident.

Sid Powers, with the fifteen buckaroos riding for him, had established a camp on the range thirty miles from town and built a trap corral with the juniper that grew on that part of the range, with long wings running out from it in the form of the letter V. He was rounding up some of the horses of his brand for the market. Mrs. Powers and the wife of one of the buckaroos had gone to the camp to cook for the outfit and have an outing. And Mrs. Powers was at an advanced stage of pregnancy.

In the evening when the boys came in from the day's ride, Mrs. Powers decided she would take a little jaunt on her husband's saddle horse which was supposed to be gentle. But the horse was not accustomed to being ridden by a woman who wore skirts, and promptly bucked her off. She received a hard fall and the shock and fright of it had evidently brought on labor. The young wrangler was the lightest man in the outfit and the only one who had not been in the saddle all day, and it fell to his lot to make the run after me. He was a little disgruntled with his job.

"I hired out to Sid to wrangle hosses an' not to be no nuss fer women havin' kids," he complained. "If Sid 's goin' to have a bunch o' skirts hangin' around camp, an' havin' babies, I'm goin' ta throw up tha job. A hoss camp ain't no place fer skirts havin' kids no way."

We drove rapidly out the road to a point about twenty miles south and east of town, and there turned off at almost a right angle to go due northeast to the horse camp. The going was slow and rough through the sage brush but it was easy to keep on the right course by watching the Big Dipper and North Star.

When we had gone what I judged to be a good ten miles, and should have been at the camp, there was no sign of a camp fire or camp. I stopped the team and asked the silent wrangler by my side where the camp was. He did not exactly know, and suggested that either he or the camp was lost, he did not know which. We discussed the situation at some length and decided we had been bearing too much toward the north.

Taking my direction from the North Star and Big Dipper, I drove a little more to the east, but after we had traveled through the sage brush a mile or two there was still no sign of what we sought. It was by that time the darkest hour of the night that comes just before the dawn.

I stopped the team to consider the situation. Although the urgency of the call was uppermost in my mind, I was caught in the spell of the enchanted desert night, and sat for a moment thrilled and silent, listening to the ponderous stillness of the sleeping desert. There was no sound but the breathing of the horses and the faint rustle of a gentle gust of desert breeze.

Then just ahead and to the right of us a violent burst of weird coyote howls suddenly shattered the tranquil stillness. The swelling, expanding waves of sound rolled across the wide desert, leaping across plain and arroyo to be dashed against the distant rim-rock and be hurled back again in reverberating, widening echoes that floated away on the thin desert air and died in the distance in thinning, expiring waves.

There were several coyotes strung along a crest of rim-rock howling in unison, but from the volume of noise they made one might have thought there were a score of them.

There was something a little different from the usual coyote howl in that weird refrain that attracted my attention. It was not the howl of the lonesome brute calling to his mate, but the audacious announcement of a band of inquisitive marauders that there was some strange and mysterious drama being enacted there on the desert that night.

"That's a different song from the one the coyote usually sings," I said to the silent buckaroo by my side.

"You're damn tootin'; I was jest thinkin' the same thing myself," he replied.

The behavior of the coyotes suggested that the camp

must be near by, so I drove on a short distance and stopped again to listen.

Then a sound like the faint echo of a woman's scream came floating to us on the thin night air, from a point far on ahead of us. It was immediately answered by another chorus of long-drawn coyote howls. We drove on toward the point the woman's scream seemed to come from.

In a few minutes we stopped to listen again and another scream came floating to us, a little plainer than the first, and we went on in that direction. We were soon between the coyotes and the point the screams were coming from; they continued to grow plainer as we advanced.

At regular intervals of a few minutes the woman screamed, and each time she was promptly answered by the coyote chorus. There were both pain and terror in those screams, echoed by the sympathetic mournfulness of the howls of the coyotes. The strange, weird repertoire might have given a lonely desert traveler the creeps, but the young buckaroo with me seemed for a moment to see a comical side to it.

"If that there skirt that 's doin' all tha squealin' an' neighin' is Sid's woman, it's a cinch that gittin' bucked off'en tha hoss didn't hurt her lungs none," he commented. "We shore won't have no trouble locatin' tha camp if her wind holds out."

Guided by the woman's screams we soon came in sight of the camp fire, which was down in a little sunken basin near a water hole, where it could not be seen from a distance. As we drove up to the camp some of the buckaroos came out to meet us and take the team, while others remained squatting on their heels around the camp fire.

Most of the buckaroos were young unmarried men without previous experience around confinement cases, and to them the situation was awkward and embarrassing. The majority of them did not go to bed after the accident, but lolled around camp, or squatted on their heels around the camp fire all night. Although they all felt great concern and keen sympathy for Mrs. Powers, they were at the same time unhappy about the situation.

I found the patient lying on a camp cot in her tent attended by Sid and the other woman of the camp. She had intended to go home in a few days for her confinement, but the accident had changed her program.

She was very nervous and terribly frightened—almost to the point of hysteria. As it was her first confinement, she did not know what labor pains were like and thought the pains she was having were due to some serious internal injury. After I had examined her carefully and assured her that she had no serious injury, her fright and nervousness subsided somewhat and she stopped screaming with each pain. After that we heard nothing more from the coyote chorus.

The long stately row of Cascade mountain peaks in the west thrust their lofty scintillating peaks high into the great ocean of gorgeous, flaming coloring, as the first level rays of the sun struck the glistening snow fields on the peaks. A moment later, the sun, like a great ball of golden fire, rose up out of the desert on the eastern horizon, painting the eastern skies in great bands of deep red, crimson, delicate pinks, and pale blue, and the long, tedious day on the desert had begun.

The patient was already tired and extremely nervous from her night of fright and pain. It was soon hot and uncomfortable in the tent, with just enough breeze to blow the sand and dust about under foot. The proximity of the horse corrals made the flies abundant and annoying. The camp cot was uncomfortable and a poor substitute for a bed. Although the labor pains were hard and frequent, the labor lasted throughout the long day, but just as darkness was again descending over the wide desert a baby boy was born and there was great rejoicing in the horse camp. I had plenty of dressings for the mother but there were no clothes for the baby. It was washed according to the custom of the time and wrapped in a blanket, squaw fashion.

One day about noon I was called in great haste to go to a ranch about thirty-five miles from town to attend the wife of a rancher, who was having a baby out in an alfalfa field where a crew of men were cutting hay.

The rancher had a hundred and fifty acres of alfalfa on a desert claim several miles from the home ranch, with no buildings on it except a small bunk house.

When he took a crew of men to the claim to cut the alfalfa, he took his wife along to cook for the haying crew. She was pregnant at about full term and the jolting of the wagon brought on labor about the time they arrived at the hay field. The pains were coming so hard and fast that they were afraid to try to get home for fear the baby would be born on the road. Enough alfalfa was hastily cut to make a good bed for the woman under the shade of a juniper tree at one side of the field, and she was placed upon it.

I made a flying trip to the alfalfa field and arrived there just in time to deliver the baby. Again I had plenty of dressings for the mother, but no clothes for the baby. I had no linen with which to change the mother's bed, but there was really no need to change it. All we had to do was to cut more alfalfa and make another bed in the shade on the other side of the tree and move the mother onto it.

She was very happy and pleased with the new baby and did not seem to mind the inconvenience of the situation in the least. She complained a little of the flies annoying her, of the grass tickling her bare legs, but otherwise she was happy and comfortable. When she had been properly installed in her new bed her husband returned to the ranch and brought the baby clothes and additional clothes for her. The mother and new baby were placed on a bed of hay in the wagon box and taken back home to the ranch.

A little before dark one evening, a frightened and excited freighter came rushing to the office all but out of breath.

"Doc, I want ya to come down to my camp right away, my woman's got this here ptomaine pizen an' I think she's dyin'," he gasped.

"Where is she?" I asked.

"She's down in the camp on the river 'bout a mile below town," he replied.

We hurried down to the place where he had gone into camp for the night with his freight outfit. He had a big freight wagon and a trailer drawn by a twelve horse team hauling a load of freight from The Dalles, on the Columbia River, to his brother's ranch near Silver Lake, two hundred and sixty miles south.

"Right after we et our dinner 'bout noon the woman begun havin' pains in her stummick, an' tha damn bellyache has been gittin' worse and worse ever since," he explained as we hurried to the camp.

"A while back tha pains was gittin' so bad God-a-mighty Hisself would 'a groaned like a sick hoss with 'em, and I give her a big jolt o' whiskey. But tha whiskey made her sick to her stummick an' she throwed it up, an' it didn't seem to help tha pains none. She 's shore mighty bad an' I know she ain't goin' to last much longer if ya don't do somethin' fer her purty quick. You gotta save her, Doc, if they 's any way in God's world to do it."

When we arrived at the camp I found a woman lying on the top of the load of freight in the wagon, rolling and moaning with pain. One look at her immediately convinced me that she was in an advanced stage of labor.

"Your wife is not poisoned," I said to the lanky freighter, "she is in labor; and she's going to have a baby in a very short time."

"Oh no, Doc, you're wrong 'bout that; that jest ain't possible," he stated with great earnestness. "We had it all figgered out before we started. The baby ain't due 'til we git down to my brother's ranch, down to Silver Lake. This here ain't no time fer her to be havin' it nohow, and I don't want her ta have it 'til we git there."

"I will agree with you that this is a poor time and place for your wife to have a baby," I said, "but it's on the way and we can't stop it now."

"You shorely must be wrong, Doc," he insisted, "it couldn't come now 'cause we ain't been married only a little over seven months."

There was no time to argue, however, for the pains were

coming hard and fast, and the patient was making quite a fuss about it. I told the dumb skinner to get the bed roll and to spread blankets on the ground by the side of the wagon as quickly as he could and help me to get his wife down from the wagon. She insisted she was going to die and did not want to be moved, but we lifted her bodily from the wagon and laid her on the blankets.

"Oh my God, my back! My belly will bust. Fer Christ's sake be careful, damn yer ornery hides; yer killin' me; I know I'm dyin'," she cried and moaned.

It was rather awkward, back-breaking work to deliver the baby on the ground, and we had no light except the little given off by the camp fire and the freighter's lantern with a badly smoked chimney. In less than an hour a baby girl arrived and did some lusty squalling, fully as much as a full term baby. All the clothes the mother had for the baby were packed away in a trunk somewhere in the load of freight.

As the night was chilly the baby was wrapped in a thick layer of absorbent cotton until its clothes could be dug out of the load. The lanky freighter was a little disgusted with his "woman" for having the baby at such an inopportune time. He watched me very closely while I was wrapping the baby in the cotton, with a scowl on his face and sarcastic remarks about its appearance, but refused to touch or handle it.

"Looks 'bout like what's left after the breakin'-up of a hard winter, only there ain't much of it," he commented with a look of disgust.

Early the next morning I went down to the camp to have a look at the mother and baby by daylight. When I came in sight of the camp I was given a mild shock. The freighter had just finished hooking up his twelve horse team and was helping some woman put the camp cooking utensils away in the grub box. For a moment I thought the woman was some one he had engaged to take care of his wife and baby, but as I came nearer I saw that it was his wife.

"What on earth do you mean by being up on your feet so soon after having a baby? Don't you know you might have a hemorrhage or some serious complication by getting up so soon?" I asked in astonishment.

"I was jest helpin' git started on the road—it's gittin' kind a late," she explained innocently. "We kaint be stoppin' here; we gotta be gittin' on down to Silver Lake."

I was a little wrought up by what I supposed was her disregard for her health, but explained as patiently as I could the risks of being up too soon after childbirth and took her husband to task for allowing her to get up. They both seemed to be a little surprised and puzzled.

"My maw never stayed in bed with none of her kids; she had four of 'em an' she was always healthy," the woman explained. "I kaint be goin' ta bed here, we gotta be gittin' on down the road to Silver Lake."

"That's right, Doc," the husband interrupted, "the woman's maw was as stout as a hoss, an' she never went to bed with none of her papooses; she was half Calapooya Injun."

That explained several things that had been a little puzzling to me at first. The squaws as a rule have no difficulty in childbirth. They go on about their usual occupations soon after the papoose arrives. I took a good look at the baby by daylight and decided that it was without doubt a full term baby, regardless of the fact they had been married only seven months.

The lanky freighter helped his wife climb up on top of the load of freight piled high in the wagon, while I held the baby. I handed the baby up to its mother; the freighter mounted his saddle on the nigh wheel horse and picked up the jerk line.

"Hi-i-ya-a, hi-ya, tighten up," he shouted, as he pulled on the jerk line, and the twelve well-trained horses leaned into their collars as one and began to pull. With the merry, musical jingle of the freighter's bells on the hames of the leaders the long team of horses swung out into the dusty road and started on the last hundred miles of their journey. I never saw the outfit again.

CHAPTER 4

Epidemic on the Frontier

DURING that first spring and summer of 1905, houses in our town of Bend were scarce and at a premium. Many families were still living in tents, marking time. There was no light, water, or sewer system. For domestic use water was hauled from the river in barrels which actually stood uncovered by the kitchen door, to be dipped into by any member of the family as occasion demanded.

Most of the tents and many of the houses were without screens; and the privy vaults, if there were any, were wide open, giving free access to the hosts of flies. The stage was all set for an epidemic and, sure enough, it came—an epidemic of typhoid fever.

The only means of preventing typhoid at that time was to discover the source of infection, then prevent its spread, for typhoid vaccine—one of the great achievements of medical science—had not yet been developed.

The water in the river was of course the first thing blamed by many of the citizens, but after some thought and investigation, I proved, to my own satisfaction at least, that the water in the river was pure and unpolluted.

The only milk to be had in town was the condensed variety of canned milk, so the milk supply could not be blamed.

Among the hosts of new settlers swarming into the

43

country from all over the West and Middle West were some who came from sections where typhoid was prevalent. Some of them had recently had the disease themselves and still carried the typhoid germs in their intestinal tracts. They were the typhoid carriers, who deposited the germs of typhoid in the open toilets and on the ground to be picked up by the common little house fly—the simuliida—and disseminated throughout the length and breadth of the land.

There had been a case of typhoid during the winter in a boy whose parents lived in two tents across the river near the upper sawmill. He had been in bed for several weeks with a virulent type of the disease, under the care of another doctor, but was not doing well. When the boy's parents heard the astonishing gossip about how "the new young Doc" at the hotel had so miraculously pulled Charlie Grant through the crisis of his serious illness, the doctor who was treating the boy was discharged and I was called.

With encouragement, cheer, and a change of treatment, the discouraged boy was soon improving; but a second case of typhoid appeared in a young woman just across the river from the boy, before he was out of bed. A few days later another case appeared, and soon after, others all over town and in widely scattered places in the country. And when the warmer weather of spring brought the flies, typhoid entered the construction camps of the irrigation company.

I appealed at once to the officers of the company to screen their meat houses, kitchens and dining tents, and to dig deep privy vaults and keep the contents covered with sand thrown into them daily to keep the flies away.

The people in town were urged to screen their houses and tents, cover their privy vaults, and swat the flies. I addressed gatherings of the farmers living on the irrigated lands and told them how to construct cisterns and reservoirs for the storage of water for domestic use, and how to prevent pollution of the irrigation ditches.

As the weather grew warmer and the flies increased, the typhoid increased, and I was soon going day and night. Some of the cases were severe and dangerous, and nearly ten per cent of them had hemorrhages. I was soon keenly aware of the tremendous load of responsibility I was carrying and could not banish my worries for a minute, whether I was asleep or awake. When I did have a chance to snatch a little sleep, I seemed to be thinking of some bad case all the while I slept.

Nursing is a very important part of the management of a typhoid case and there was not a graduate nurse in the county; the so-called practical nurses were few. In most cases the patient depended on some member of his family to nurse him.

With no milk, eggs, or fruit juices available, it was almost impossible to find suitable nourishment for the patients. Ice was scarce and hard to get.

There were some caves fourteen miles southeast of town, called the ice caves, where ice was continually forming on the floor of the caves. But this was difficult to get as it had to be chopped out of the floor of the caves, hoisted to the surface, then hauled to town.

In the beginning I saw every typhoid patient at least once a day; but I was soon so busy that I could see some of them only every second or third day and some of those in the country only once a week. When the epidemic was at its height I was so busy that I was obliged to treat some of the country cases entirely by telephone, without seeing them at all.

In such cases the person who nursed the patient answered my questions and gave me the pulse, temperature, and other symptoms by telephone. I then gave them directions and sent medicine by stage or messenger.

A rancher living much nearer to other doctors than to me insisted that I attend his daughter who was just coming down with typhoid. I explained to him fully why I could not take another case and asked him to call one of the doctors nearer to her, but he could not seem to understand my situation.

He remained in the office so long arguing with me and was taking up so much of my time that I finally frantically and foolishly promised I would see the girl just once, if he would then call another doctor to finish the case.

The girl's mother would not abide by her husband's agreement, however, and insisted that I continue on the case. I managed to see the girl only three times during her six weeks' illness, but she had no complications and made a good recovery. The mother was not only dissatisfied because I did not make more calls, but mad, and objected to paying the bill. Moreover, she stayed mad and said all kinds of nasty things about me. Her selfishness seemed to destroy her reasonableness completely.

At my first call on each typhoid case, I gave the person responsible for the nursing complete instructions in writing for the care and feeding of the patient, with a complete list of all foods allowed. One hard and fast rule was that no patient with a particle of fever was allowed any solid food. It was difficult to make people understand that liquids were food, that a patient would not die even if he had no food of any kind for a week, or even longer. In some cases patients did well who took nothing but water for periods of eight or ten days. In spite of all my pains and written instructions there were many mistakes and misunderstandings regarding diet.

The first case to appear in the construction camps was that of a lad of nineteen whose parents lived in town. He had been in bed with fever in the camp a few days before he was taken to his home, where I first saw him the day he arrived.

His abdomen was much more tender and distended and his temperature higher than it should have been so early in the course of the disease. I supposed it was due to the food he had been given in the camp and expected these conditions to improve after a few days of proper treatment. But at the end of a week there was not much change.

I was a little puzzled and frankly told his mother, who was nursing him, that I did not understand why it should be so and asked her what he had had to eat that day.

"Oh, nothing, nothing at all," she replied.

The next day at my regular visit I asked the same question and received the same reply. Still his abdomen was greatly distended and his temperature above a hundred and five. I could not understand it.

"What?" I said, "hasn't he taken any nourishment at all the last two days?"

"Oh, yes," she said, "he has taken lots of that broth you said he could have, but he hasn't had a thing to eat."

Then it began to dawn on me that when she said he hadn't had anything to eat she meant he had taken no solid food.

"He had quite a crying spell today," his mother continued. "It may be that is what made his fever so high. I ran out of candy today and he didn't have any candy to take his medicine with and he made a terrible fuss about it."

The mystery was solved. She had been giving him candy—and chocolates at that—with each dose of medicine, to take away the bitter taste.

I blew up—I couldn't help it—and told the poor, worried woman several things she'll never forget. I also ridiculed the big husky youth for being such a baby that he could not take medicine without candy. He was given no more candy; much of the bloat in his abdomen disappeared and his temperature receded to the usual level of cases at that period of the disease.

One of the engineers of the irrigation company had a case of mild or ambulatory typhoid, sometimes called walking typhoid. He had been running a slight fever for several days in one of the construction camps, but did not go to bed. As soon as I examined him in the office he was sent to bed in a room in the hotel where one of his friends living there could look after him part of the time.

Although his fever was not high he became irrational at times. One hot day he decided that the hotel room was too hot for comfort, that he would be more comfortable under the shade of a tree down on the river bank.

He got out of bed when there was no one in the room and partially dressed himself by putting on his shirt and boots, but forgot the remainder of his clothing. He draped the bed sheet around his shoulders with most of it hanging down his back, and wandered hatless down the back stairs of the hotel and out onto the street. Instead of traveling toward the river, he went for a block in the opposite direction to a house which had a grassy lawn and some shade trees in the front yard.

Some of the church ladies were holding a gathering in the house when he entered the yard wandering around under a tree looking for a soft spot on which to stretch his wabbly, unclad legs. One of the ladies happened to look out of the window and saw him. She let out a shriek that could be heard clear back to the hotel, and pandemonium broke loose.

The gathering crowd and the commotion in the house roused the poor half-clad engineer from his trance and he began to suspect that he was in the wrong pew, or the wrong yard, and that he was not properly clad for whatever the occasion was.

While he was vainly trying to hide behind himself and readjust the sheet that was mostly hanging down his back, some of his friends recognized him and assisted him back to the hotel. He seemed none the worse for the experience when I saw him later in the day, but I provided him with a nurse who could stay with him at all times and he made an uneventful recovery.

One of the cases that was treated entirely by telephone was of the mild type also, but the engineer's case was the only mild one I *saw;* all the others were arduous or severe.

As summer came on and the temperature was high at mid-day while the nights were cool or even frosty, a virulent type of dysentery began to rage, one which was particularly severe on the babies and children.

The water in the river was again blamed for the dysentery, but I soon discovered that the babies who drank nothing but boiled water had the dysentery just as frequently as the others. Investigation convinced me that the infection was spread by the flies, especially a little black fly known as the diptera, as well as by the simuliida, or common house fly. It was quite another matter to convince some of the wiser ones of that fact, however, but when the cold weather in the fall came and the flies disappeared, the dysentery ceased.

My first severe case of dysentery was the one-year-old son of a Scandinavian woman who had just arrived in town after a long, hot journey. She came to the office one morning and asked for medicine for both herself and the baby. The following morning she came back to the office again.

"Dot bane fine medsin wot you givf me; I bane all right today; but dot medsin wot you givf Ole, it bane no goot. Ole he bane worst today," she explained.

I told her it would be best for me to see Ole; that I would come to her house shortly and sent her back home.

Ole, a big, husky, one-year-old boy, still unweaned and nursing the breast, was vomiting his last nursing as I entered. He vomited while his mother was at the office and she nursed him again just as soon as she returned! It was that nursing he was throwing up in big curds and chunks as I came in. Immediately after the vomiting ceased his mother started to nurse him again!

I stopped his nursing immediately and examined him.

He was having frequent bowel discharges and had vomited several times that morning, and his mother had allowed him to nurse each time as soon as the vomiting ceased. He was very sick, had a very high fever, and was badly dehydrated.

I gave his mother careful instructions for his care and told her not to allow him to nurse or to give him food of any kind until I called again late in the afternoon. I left medicine and told her to give him a teaspoonful of it every hour, and to give him all the water he could take at frequent intervals. I repeated my instructions and wrote them on paper, cautioning her again not to nurse him or give him any food. I was about to leave when she stopped me.

"Vy mister doc-a-tor, if I not feed Ole anyting he vill starvf. I havf to give him nurse to givf him strenghl"

I carefully explained to her that the food Ole took did not give him any strength as it could not even start to digest; that it only irritated his stomach and made him all the sicker. She listened attentively until I finished and I thought she understood.

"Ya, ya, but if I not give Ole nurse he vill starvf," she stated conclusively.

Again and again I explained until I thought she was convinced, and then went on to make other calls.

The baby was so very sick that I was worried about him and returned to see him earlier in the afternoon than I had first intended. I got back to the house just as he was throwing up a lot of curdled milk. The mother admitted she had nursed him several times during my absence, and that he had vomited after each nursing.

"If you expect me to treat this baby you will have to follow my instructions or I will quit the case," I said rather hotly.

"Vell quit de case," she retorted. "You doan havf to bane a doc-a-torin' Ole, I vill git 'noder doc-a-tor. Dere bane some leddies from de church here dis afternoon wot tell me 'bout Mister Doc-a-tor Blank. He bane older dan you an' know more 'bout doc-a-torin' bebbies, an' he bane nize Christin schentlemens wot go to schurch, an' de leddies say you doan go to schurch. I doan tink you know much bout a doc-a-torin' bebbies—you too young."

"Well, you call Doctor Blank right away and do exactly as he tells you to or Ole will die. He is a very sick baby," I said.

I do not know whether she followed the instructions of the other doctor, but about a week later a frantic call came for me to see the baby. The front door was open when I arrived at the house and there was no one in sight. I entered without knocking and saw the baby lying in his crib, dead. There was the sound of voices and a woman crying in the next room. I tiptoed over to the door and peeped in. The other doctor was standing in the center of the room with his arms around the baby's mother; she was crying on his shoulder.

"It is the Lord's will, dear sister," he said impressively. "The Lord giveth and the Lord taketh away. Blessed be the name of the Lord." The doctor was also a preacher and sometimes handed out spiritual advice along with his pills.

I decided that was no place for me and speedily withdrew without making my presence known.

The poor mother was resentful and rebellious because

she believed the Lord had deprived her of her only child. I was told that she collapsed in the cemetery at the funeral the next day and was taken home raving and hysterical. She became so violent during the night that her brother became alarmed and sent for me, but I was away in the country.

To my surprise the mother herself sent for me a day later and when I arrived at her house I discovered the other doctor had been there before me. The mother was highly excited and a little irrational, with her voice high pitched and strident, and a wild, unnatural glitter in her eyes.

She said she had sent for me because she wanted to tell me how happy she was. The other doctor had convinced her she should be the happiest woman in the world because the Lord had chosen her from among all the millions of mothers in the whole world and given her the rare privilege of serving Him by sacrificing the one thing dearest to her. I gave her a hypodermic at once.

That was the first time I had been discharged from a case, and I felt the sting and humiliation of defeat very keenly. I told myself that it was all due to the ignorance of the mother and to no fault of mine, but I felt chagrined and humiliated just the same.

The baby was as near a perfect physical specimen of babyhood as any I ever saw. His death was due entirely to the ignorance and stubbornness of his mother. If the other doctor had been in any way responsible for it, he certainly had an ingenious alibi.

The thought that people might not trust me and have confidence in my ability never occurred to me before I began to practice. No doubt my youthful appearance was a handicap as the belief was prevalent that the older the doctor was, the more he knew. It was also a rude surprise to me to discover how little some people appreciated what was done for them. My preconceived ideas and ideals were continually receiving rude jolts. I was constantly being shocked by the ignorance I came in contact with. Ignorance is the greatest obstacle with which a doctor has to contend. Lack of confidence on the part of the patient is the next greatest. It deprives the patient of the full measure of benefit he would otherwise receive and it is a blight on the morale of the doctor, impairing his efficiency.

The number of babies desperately sick with dysentery increased as the weather grew hotter. Many adults had dysentery also, but there were no deaths among them.

In the meantime the obstetrical mill was grinding steadily and ceaselessly on, but the peak of production in babies was not reached until the third year of my practice.

By the middle of spring the heavy construction work on the large irrigation canals near town was completed and the camps closed. The company moved its offices and headquarters to a point on the desert near one of its large canals about twenty miles north, where two roads crossed, and there the new town of Redmond sprung up and began to grow.

The hundreds of laborers who had made Bend and the adjacent camps their headquarters soon drifted to Redmond and the new construction camps near by. Most of the gamblers, tin horns, sporting girls and transients of all kinds, followed the big payroll to Redmond. The roaring, booming town of Bend began to decline into a more prosaic existence.

Office and city practice dwindled, but the country work increased by leaps and bounds. With the numerous typhoid and dysentery cases scattered all over the country, the countless confinements, the usual run of sickness and accident cases, I was continually on the go at top speed, day and night.

Oregon was famous for her range horses in those days; there were no better horses any place in the world, though there were two classes of them. The inferior was a breed of native pony of small size and bone, usually called fuzz tail or cayuse, used by the Indians. The better class resulted when the horse breeders began to turn stallions of thoroughbred blood on the range. I found that the better range horse, raised on the bunch grass of the desert, had more stamina and endurance than had the standard bred horses that I had been accustomed to in the Middle West, fed on oats and timothy hay. If the bunch grassers from the range were warmed up properly at the start, they could dust along at a ten-mile-an-hour clip all day long, and after a feed of grain and a little rest be ready for the return trip. Calls to patients fifty and seventy-five miles from town were commonplace, and I sometimes went a hundred miles and more to see a patient.

A sheriff chasing a criminal or a doctor on a long hurry call could stop at any of the big ranches and get a fresh mount or team if need be. There were standing orders on all the big ranches to give the sheriff and the doctor the best saddle horse or driving team on the ranch in case a change was needed; to have his stock in the best condition possible when he came back to pick them up on the return trip. That helped us to make long trips in remarkably short time.

With the ever-swelling flood of typhoid and dysentery cases scattered all over the country, and many of them far from town, I spent most of my time in the buggy.

I could save much time by doing my work in town in the daytime and spending the night going to country patients. Very few indeed were the nights I did not drive all night. Had it not been for the worries and heavy responsibilities and the terrific strain I labored under, I would have enjoyed those enchanting nights on the sleeping desert, but I always had serious cases to worry me. I hired all of my horses from one of the livery stables in town, where I could always get an extra good team on a moment's notice.

Bands of wild range horses were frequently driven through town on the way to the outside markets. The liveryman usually selected what he wanted from the best of these herds and immediately began to break them. When a new team had been hitched to a heavy breaking wagon until they were thought to be sufficiently bridlewise, they were then given to me to drive on the first long, hard trip I had to make. After one of those drives on a hurry call, the team usually came back to the barn tamer and better broken than when they started out. I helped the liveryman break a good many of his horses that way and thoroughly enjoyed doing it. I had been raised with horses back in Missouri and was very fond of them.

With all the long hard drives I was compelled to make under all sorts of conditions, and in all kinds of weather, I had the good fortune never to have a horse get sick on the road, never to let a team of wild ones get away from me. If the team ran away, as sometimes it did, I always managed to stick with them.

Driving across the desert on a hot summer day was no pleasure trip. The buggy wheels and horses' hoofs kicked up a great cloud of fine, powdery dust that enveloped the team and buggy and was carried along with us all day by the draft of air created by our rapid movement, unless it was blown aside by a breeze from the right direction. The dry dust filled the eyes, nose, mouth, and throat, filtered down into the lungs, penetrated all clothing; there was no means of escaping it.

I did as much of my driving as possible at night in the summer, as the dust did not fly so badly in the more humid night air and it was cooler for the horses. During the day I saw all my patients in town and then hurried off to my patients in the country, usually driving all night.

I always drove alone, except on the very few occasions when someone went along to pilot me to a camp on the desert or some out-of-the-way place far from the traveled road. I was often asked why I did not have a driver so I could sleep more in the buggy. I usually told people that no one drove to suit me. But that was not the real reason. I wanted to be alone with my thoughts. Those enchanting desert nights inspired dreams I could not even begin to describe; they could only be experienced. The men who did go with me on a few occasions, with one exception, seemed to be suffering with a torrent of undelivered palaver; they seemed to desire nothing but continuous pow-wow. One talked of money, women, and drink; another of cattle, ranches, and horses; another of woman and politics. But it was all senseless chatter; I wanted to think.

I was weighted down with an avalanche of worries and tremendous responsibilities. Awake or asleep there was always that vivid picture on my conscious or subconscious mind of some patient I feared might die. I wondered if I had done exactly the proper thing for him, or if I had left something undone. I had no chance even to look at a medical journal, and I wondered if there was some new treatment for his ailment that I did not know about. I wondered what some master physician in the city would do next in such a case.

"And thoughts on thoughts, a countless throng,
Rushed, chasing countless thoughts along."

Sometimes I went to bed, after going day and night for several days without having my clothes off, thinking and worrying about some desperately sick patient, a little puzzled to know just what to do next. From sheer exhaustion I would fall into a light troubled sleep, but all the while conscious of seeing and thinking about the patient.

After a time I would wake with a sudden start, the problem solved and my mind clear, knowing exactly what I should do next. Then I could no longer rest or sleep until I got up and hurried off to the patient to start the additional treatment. I have sometimes done my best thinking in that fashion when I was apparently asleep.

That sort of living is a killing, soul-wearing existence, unless one has within him that inexplicable, tremendous urge that makes even the hardships a part of its fascination. The money a doctor receives for his work and worry is mighty insignificant pay at best and no recompense at all if there is not some understanding and appreciation to go with it.

But the thought of quitting never occurred to me. That indefinable, overpowering urge that made me so desperately want to be a doctor when I was still a small boy seemed to grow instead of diminish. I was always completely absorbed in my work.

CHAPTER 5

Delivery by Telephone

I WAS so interested in the booming town, so fascinated
with the wild west country, so enmeshed in the dizzy
whirl of my practice, with its endless problems and responsibilities, that spring flew by before I was aware of
it. With the loss of the big payroll, Bend was undergoing
a slow and painful decline. But with more idle time on
their hands, the Bend boosters talked all the time of the
coming railroad, although it seemed to be as far away as
ever.

In the midst of the depression the governor of the
State of Oregon announced that he and the other mem-
bers of the State Land Board would visit Bend on the
Fourth of July to inspect the new irrigation project.

That was a welcome cue to the enterprising Bend
boosters and to the Commercial Club. They immediately
held a big pow-wow and decided to celebrate the double
occasion with a three-day Fourth of July celebration and
trout barbecue, beginning on the third. Committees were
appointed, huge advertising placards were posted, and
the great event was advertised far and wide. The whole
Northwest was invited and all visitors were promised all
the trout they could eat for three days, free.

Three-day Fourth of July celebrations were not unusual along the sparsely settled frontier in the horse-and-buggy days where many of the visitors traveled long distances to attend; but a trout barbecue was something really distinctive, something the wide-awake boosters knew no other town in that part of the state could offer.

The big event was pulled off according to schedule, with hundreds of visitors present from all points within a radius of two or three hundred miles, coming in wagons, buckboards, by stage or horseback. There were then no automobiles.

There were speeches by the distinguished guests, foot races, horse races, athletic and sporting events, a competitive shooting tournament open to all, and of course bronco-riding contests. No celebration of any sort on the frontier was complete without a bronco-busting circus.

A large dance floor was constructed under the big pine trees at the upper end of the principal business street, and a dance began on the third which continued without a pause until the evening of the fifth.

The four men of the fish committee, who provided the fish for the occasion, fished from daylight until dark for three days and caught thirty-six hundred and seventy-five trout, all over twelve inches. They used the regulation light trout tackle with two flies on their leaders and often caught two at a cast. Most of the catch were of the rainbow variety, or redsides, as they were called; but there were some cutthroat, silversides, and Dolly Varden, or lake trout, some of which were nearly three feet long. I will not attempt to state how much some of the larger rainbow weighed for fear the reader may think I am telling a fish story.

One enterprising citizen went to the woods the day be-

fore the celebration began and killed two fat black bears
to provide bear steaks for those who preferred bear to
trout. There was plenty for all and the celebration was a
howling success.

That was during my first year (1905) and there was no
law regulating the number of trout any man was allowed
to catch in a day. A few years later, a law was passed
limiting the number caught by one person in a day to a
hundred and twenty-five; but even so there were no game
wardens to enforce the laws.

There was a big platter of fried trout on each table at
the hotel throughout the spring and summer, which was
replenished as fast as it was depleted, and everyone
helped himself to all he wanted.

When the trout disappeared from the tables at the end
of summer, venison appeared; we called it "Oregon Ranch
Veal." Juicy steaks and tender roasts from the big Oregon
mule deer were served to the hotel guests all winter.
There was an open season on deer from August until
some time in October, but no one paid much attention to
the law.

The deer stayed pretty well up in the mountains during
the summer and open season, but with the first snows in
the fall they started to drift lower down. As the snow
deepened in the higher altitudes they came down to the
edge of the timber and out onto the desert where they
stayed fat and sleek all winter, browsing on the tender
twigs of the chemiso brush.

When the big Fourth of July celebration was over, the
little town lapsed into deeper lassitude than before, with
a dwindling population. The two doctors who were prac-

ticing in the town when I came left for new locations about that time, and I was the only practicing physician left. It was then that I saw my first case of puerperal eclampsia (convulsions at childbirth).

The dysentery and typhoid cases had been increasing and I was going as fast as I could travel, day and night. At the end of a trying week, I had a long, tedious confinement case on Sunday night. All day Monday I was hurrying around to country cases without a moment's rest. Monday night I had another long, troublesome confinement, and was just preparing to do a forceps delivery at daylight when a man who lived a block from tho house where I was came after me.

His wife had been under my care since the beginning of her pregnancy, and had been unusually well throughout. She had a few light labor pains in the night but she fell asleep for a while and awoke at daylight with an excruciating headache.

I gave the husband medicine to give to her for the headache and told him I would come and see his wife as soon as I was through with the case I was on. I had just finished the forceps delivery when the man came running back for me greatly excited.

"For God's sake come quick, Doc, come quick," he shouted, and grabbing me by the arm started running to his home. I asked him several times what the trouble was as he dragged me along on the run, but he only continued shouting, "For God's sake, come quick." I was too tired to run as fast as he wanted to go, so jerked loose from his vise-like grip, and followed him on the run.

When I rushed into his wife's bedroom and saw her in the throes of a horrible convulsion, I forgot I was tired.

Labor had barely started but she was having a convulsion every twenty or thirty minutes.

I hurried the labor along as fast as I could and after three desperate hours delivered a dead baby with the forceps. She had a frightful hemorrhage immediately after the delivery and another convulsion. After the hemorrhage was at last under control the convulsions ceased and in a few hours she slowly began to regain consciousness. She made a good recovery and about a year later, after a normal labor, gave birth to a normal baby.

That case came as a complete surprise and without the slightest warning. The woman had been at the office only three days before her illness, feeling unusually well. At that time there was no albumin in her urine, which is usually one of the very first symptoms of impending eclampsia.

We know today that there is usually a rise in the blood pressure as eclampsia develops, but at that time little was known about blood pressure, and the instruments for taking it had not been invented. There might have been an increase in her pressure when she was at the office, but there was no outward sign of it, and she felt happy and well.

After that case occurred I secured all the available literature on eclampsia and studied it in the buggy as I drove to the country. It was well that I did so, for I had cases of it frequently. There was a greater percentage of eclampsia in that country than in most other places. The great variation between day and night temperatures and the lack of calcium in the water and soil might have had something to do with it. The toxins (poisons) in the blood stream which accompany eclampsia usually kill the baby, but many of the mothers survive, although the mortality is very high.

The weather grew hotter as summer advanced, the number of typhoid cases continued to mount, and more and more babies came down with dysentery. I had more sick patients to look after than one man could take care of properly. Especially as they were scattered over such a large territory. I desperately hoped that the women would declare a truce on having so many babies for a little while, but it was a vain hope.

One hot summer morning, a few days after the eclampsia case, I returned to the office from a long country trip and was about to wash the dust out of my eyes, nose, and mouth when an urgent call came from the end of a local telephone line. A woman in a camp at a water hole on the desert, forty-five miles from town, was having a hemorrhage at childbirth. I telephoned the livery stable for a team for a long hurry call, grabbed up my bags and rushed down to the street in front of the office to wait.

It so happened that the men at the stable who broke the wild horses had just hitched a team of wild broncos they were breaking to a buggy for the first time. They had been hitched to a heavy breaking wagon a few times and were supposed to be bridlewise.

With one man in the buggy driving and a man leading each horse by the bridle, the team was brought to the office immediately. Each horse had a length of strong rope tied securely around his neck for me to tie them with when I arrived at my destination. A man stood at the head of each horse holding him by the bridle while I loaded my bags and got a good hold on the lines. When all was ready I sang out, "let 'em go," and we went down the road in a cloud of dust, with the horses on a dead run.

They were bridlewise enough so I could keep them in the road, but I could not hold them in as much as I wanted to, to allow them to warm up properly for the long hard forty-five mile drive. They pulled the buggy by the reins for several miles until my arms ached, and we made the forty-five miles to the water hole in a little less than four hours. That was some traveling with a team and buggy.

The water hole was situated in an old dry river bed, in a shallow valley at the edge of a wide plain where there had been no water above the surface for centuries. A shallow well had been dug down to water which seeped over the bed rock in the old river bed. Low juniper ridges ran off from the edge of the plain at a right angle.

I drove along between two of these ridges toward the water hole until I saw the top of a tent and heard a bedlam of human voices, crying, wailing, and cursing.

The noise and the smell of blood frightened the horses, and I got out and tied them securely to a juniper tree, unhitching them from the buggy.

I took my obstetrical bag and walked out onto the edge of the plain toward the water hole. There a sight met my eyes that I shall never forget.

On the bare simmering sand near the water hole, quailing under the hot mid-day sun, stood a tent. In front on the hot sand lay the body of an almost naked woman smeared with sand and blood from head to feet. Grouped around it in a circle were eight ragged, dirty children, from three to eighteen years old, crying and wailing in the most abject misery and grief. A tall, powerfully built man, wild-eyed, ragged and dirty, with a three-weeks' growth of beard, the wide brim of his sombrero flopping in time with his movements, was doing the Piute War Dance around the children. He held a naked unwashed baby in his left arm and was brandishing a big six-shooter at the sky with his right hand. In a vituperative stream of blood-curdling profanity he threatened all the gods in Heaven and defied Jesus Christ to come down to earth in person and fight him in mortal combat. From the dead woman's body a trail of blood led back into the tent. It was hard to realize that all of the blood on the sand had come from one human body. It was a pathetic, ghastly and soul-sickening sight.

Several years before this man had located on a tract of vacant public lands to the east of the Blue Mountains. He had bought more land around it to establish a sheep ranch; but he had become gradually surrounded by cattle outfits as the range became crowded. He had tried to stay in the sheep business contrary to the "suggestions" of the cattle men who surrounded him, and trouble began to assail him.

His leg was broken by the kick of a horse; there was sickness in the family and he had financial troubles. There were range disputes, in one of which his oldest son had been killed. He finally lost his sheep and ranch to satisfy a mortgage. At last he was forced out and gave up, loaded what was left of his belongings and his family into two wagons, and started for his brother's ranch in northern California.

When they arrived at the water hole on the desert his wife told him they had better camp there since she felt her confinement was approaching. She had given birth to nine children and with some of them she had not been attended by a doctor. They had lived far from town. Never having had trouble at any of her previous labors, she was not in the least apprehensive this time, was not afraid to go through her confinement without a doctor.

Labor came on in the night and some time about daylight she gave birth to a fine boy. But the placenta (afterbirth) did not deliver as it should have. For a time this did not worry them and they tried for a few hours, by the simple methods they knew, to deliver the afterbirth, but without success.

They finally became worried; and the husband, excited and a little rattled, took hold of the umbilical cord and gave a hard pull. The woman screamed and the blood came with a gush. They were both frightened by the alarming hemorrhage and did not know what to do. The husband, leaving the oldest boy in charge of things, jumped on a horse and rode to the nearest ranch, fifteen miles away, to get help and call a doctor.

The woman, lying on a mattress in the tent, soon began to feel faint from the heat and loss of blood, and asked the boy to help her outside. Leaving a trail of blood behind her, she crawled on her hands and knees outside of the tent, where she wallowed around in the sand until she expired from loss of blood.

I finally managed to quiet the husband with hypodermics, and got the gun away from him, for I feared he might kill himself and the children. The long siege of troubles he had been through was more than he could endure. His nerves had snapped under the last shock.

I started some of the children carrying water from the water hole, washed and dressed the baby, who seemed none the worse because of delayed attention. I had begun to clean up the corpse when some people from the ranch arrived to help.

With the assistance of some of the men, I managed to get my wild team of broncos hitched to the buggy again without mishap. Leaving the bereaved family to the care of the kind-hearted ranchers, I drove back to town in the evening and never saw any of the family again.

The tough, wild broncos were apparently unhurt by the hard race to the water hole—I think it was the hardest drive I ever had to make—but they were pretty well subdued by the time I got back to the livery stable with them.

For days and days after that drive, I could see that tragic scene at the water hole every time I closed my eyes. But the continuous grind, the dizzy rush and whirl of work, with the worries and responsibility of many serious cases, diverted my thoughts somewhat; and there were occasional bits of comedy to help lighten the tremendous strain I was under. Sometimes my valued friend and indispensable aid, Miss Hastings in the central telephone office, helped me to get a little rest.

Miss Hastings knew of all of my goings and comings, both by day and by night, and she would always get a call through to me promptly for anyone in distress if I was anywhere within a hundred miles and could be reached by telephone. Sometimes, when I had been going for days and days with little rest or sleep, she would not ring me for an hour, while I locked the door to the office and slept. When the hour was up she would call me and give me the messages that had come in while I slept.

About a week after the case at the water hole I got back to the office one evening at five, tired out and all in, and arranged with Miss Hastings to lock the door so that I could sleep until six. But at five-thirty she woke me for an urgent call from a ranch forty-five miles northwest of town. A few minutes after I started, a woman living on a ranch thirty-five miles upriver south of town decided she was going to have a baby that night and wanted me to attend her. Her telephone was on a party line connecting about a dozen ranches along the river, with the central office in town. Each ranch on the party line had its own call of so many long and short rings, so that any ranch could get any other ranch on the line without calling central. Listening in to the conversations going up and down the line was a favorite pastime on all ranches. I had noticed a wad of cotton, just the proper size to plug the transmitter, reposing on top of every telephone box. When a member of the household listened in on the line, he plugged the transmitter with the cotton so he could repeat what he heard to the rest of the family without being heard by those talking on the line. When the ranch up the river called, every ranch on the line heard Miss Hastings say I had started to a ranch forty-five miles in the opposite direction but that she would intercept me as soon as she could.

At the first ranch I came to, just ten miles out, the rancher was waiting in the road and held my team while I went into the house to telephone. The telephone there was on a party line connecting several farms and ranches on the west side of the river with the little town of Laidlaw, seven miles down the river from Bend. The only telephone in Laidlaw was in the general store, and the storekeeper acted as hello-girl.

I called the storekeeper in Laidlaw and had him call

Miss Hastings over a second line to ask her what she wanted of me. She told him about the woman on the ranch up the river who wanted me to deliver her baby that night. He relayed the information to me.

I sent word back that I could not leave the call I was on, because the case was urgent; but I gave instructions for the preparation of the woman and the management of the first stage of labor. Miss Hastings relayed a lot of questions the people in charge of the case asked, and I answered them all in layman's language.

All the conversation was going over three different telephone lines (all party lines), and all receivers were down, with people listening in.

The telephoning took considerable time because it all had to be twice relayed, but I made it as short as possible and hurried on to my call.

At the next ranch I came to, just seven miles farther on the road, the rancher was waiting in the road to call me to the telephone again. The labor seemed to be progressing satisfactorily, but those in charge wanted more information and directions. All the conversations from this point again traveled over all three party lines. The ranchers over a wide territory were enjoying some very unusual entertainment, at the same time receiving a practical lesson in obstetrics.

Some of my explicit language must have been shocking and embarrassing to the silvery-haired Miss Hastings, who was quite without obstetrical experience, but she stuck gamely to her post and repeated every word without hesitation or reservation.

Seven miles beyond the second ranch I came to the little town of Sisters, where the telephone I was called to was in the general store. From there I talked directly to Miss Hastings, and only two lines were used, but I had to speak rather loudly and the proprietor and all the village loafers, who were spitting tobacco juice at the sawdust box near the stove, heard all I said. They all seemed to get a big kick out of the conversation and would have detained me indefinitely with their questions had I not hurried on.

When I arrived at my destination, I stayed there only long enough to attend to the patient properly, stopping to telephone only once on my way back to town.

When I got back to the livery stable about daylight, a fresh team was all harnessed and waiting. Instead of closing the telephone office at nine o'clock, as usual, Miss Hastings had stayed until late to keep me in touch with the confinement case, and left the upriver line connected with the livery stable when she went home. I called the ranch and found that the baby had been born but the afterbirth not delivered. I started for the ranch immediately. There I delivered the afterbirth, sewed up an extensive laceration, and left the mother and a normal baby boy in good condition.

On my way back to town I was stopped at nearly every ranch I passed by inquisitive and interested ranchers who were anxious to know how the case came out. They all admitted listening in on the line and offered no apologies for doing so. Some described the reactions of various members of the family to the conversation and one old wag insisted he could hear Miss Hastings blushing over the wire. A confinement by telephone was novel, and rather exciting, and was a major topic of conversation throughout the community for some time. Many months after the incident Miss Hastings told me it was the most embarrassing experience of her life.

By the middle of summer the confinement cases were becoming so numerous that they were annoying—not because I disliked them but because they took so much time. There were periods when I was so rushed I did not have time to put charges on the books for the calls I made or make out birth certificates for all the babies that were born. If the father or some other member of the family came to the office and paid the twenty-five dollar fee for my services, I always took the time to make out a birth certificate. The majority of those who did not pay received no birth certificate.

Of late years I frequently get letters from former confinement patients or relatives asking for a birth certificate for some baby I delivered and issued no certificate for during those busy times. When the case is looked up in the old ledger, I invariably find the baby had not been paid for. I usually write the person who has asked for the certificate and tell them I will be glad to issue one if the unpaid balance is forwarded. As a rule I hear nothing more from them; they prefer to go without the certificate. They know the account is outlawed and is not collectible by process of law.

The percentage of eclampsia cases was very high in that country, and it is strange I did not have the first case until I had practiced six months: they came more frequently ever after and I came to dislike those cases more than anything else in practice. It was a rare thing for a baby to survive a convulsion in the mother in those days, and a large percentage of the mothers died, but for some unknown reason the first two mothers survived. Trouble came on later.

The first woman that I attended to die with convulsions was a woman who lived on a homestead fifty miles from town whom I saw for the first time when called to deliver her.

The labor was not far advanced when I arrived at daylight. Her husband left a short time later with his team and wagon, to go for a neighbor woman who lived eight miles away, to come and act as nurse.

A few minutes later the woman developed a terrific headache, said she could not see well. I knew what that meant and began at once to hurry the labor along. In a short time she began having hard convulsions.

I had hurried the labor and was ready to do a forceps delivery when the husband and neighbor nurse arrived. The husband was astounded when he saw his wife having a convulsion and could not be made to understand what was happening. He had never heard of eclampsia, and thought I had done something, or left something undone, to cause the convulsions. The neighbor woman was little help, and the terrified husband worse than no help, but the delivery was accomplished with dispatch. The convulsions continued, however, in spite of all that was done.

If there is anything that will make a man tremble in his boots and wonder why he ever studied medicine, it is an eclampsia case in a little cramped desert shack without facilities, miles from nowhere, and no one to help or give an anaesthetic. Add to that, not only lack of confidence but suspicion in the mind of the stranger you are working for, and the strain you work under is terrific.

The husband remained dazed, terrified, and suspicious, but I finally persuaded him to send to the county seat, eighty-five miles away, for a doctor for consultation.

I worked incessantly with the woman all that day and all night until the other doctor arrived at daylight, but the convulsions did not abate. She finally lapsed into a deep coma and died.

The other doctor explained the case to the bereaved husband, patiently answered all of his questions, and exonerated me from all blame, but the man could not seem to rid his mind of the belief that I was to blame in some way for the death of his wife. He paid no attention to the bills I sent him, or the letters I wrote. He finally disposed of his homestead and left the country without paying me.

One thing that impressed me deeply in connection with the large number of baby cases I attended was the haphazard and careless manner in which birth and creation are carried on in the human race. Many of the babies I delivered were not wanted but were merely the result of accident. Some of the accidental babies were later valued, or perhaps even loved and cherished, but if the parents had had their wish in the beginning, the babies would never have been born. Surely birth control would be of benefit to the human race. If for no other reason it would be an incalculable blessing through the number of abortions it would prevent.

I naturally expected to have abortion cases to attend, but I was surprised at the number of them, both in town and in the country.

The cases of self-induced abortions, too far out in the country to be watched closely, were always a source of worry, and I disliked them accordingly. There was always the danger of hemorrhage and infection.

The safest treatment for the incomplete, self-induced abortions was to operate and empty the uterus by curettage; and that was the treatment I usually gave them. The patient was put on the kitchen table and, if there was no one to give an anaesthetic, the patient was allowed to take chloroform by the drinking-glass method I have described.

One of the most remarkable things in connection with my obstetrical experience was the fact that I never had a single case of infection at the time of childbirth. In fact I never saw a case of puerperal infection in any of the women I confined in all sorts of places and under a great variety of adverse conditions.

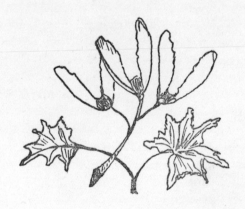

CHAPTER 6

My First Death

AFTER the big Fourth of July celebration the town gradually became as quiet as it had been boisterous in the spring. Idle real-estate dealers, business men, merchants with empty stores, had plenty of time to go fishing or talk optimistically of the railroad that was sure to come some day. The heat waves danced in the empty streets as the dust grew drier and deeper and the typhoid and dysentery cases continued to mount.

Being the only practicing physician in town after the two doctors left, I tried to answer all the calls that came in; but I was sometimes too busy to see everyone who called me. I spent most of my time in the buggy rushing around among my patients scattered all over the country. There were days at a time when I did not have my clothes off or go to bed. Sometimes I fell asleep and dozed while sitting by the bedside of a patient; but most of the sleep I managed to get was in the buggy while driving. The weeks flew by like a crazy nightmare—weeks of weariness, apprehension and worry, during which I not only lost much sleep but missed many meals.

On the way out to see a patient I rarely slept. I was always in a hurry with my attention centered on the driving and the horses. After the call had been made and I was on the way home I used to tie the reins together, one

77

on the inside, the other on the outside of the buggy whip, which was left standing in its socket on the dashboard. Then I would lean against the back of the seat and doze.

As the doze deepened into sleep my hand would gradually relax and the reins begin to slip from my grasp. Just as they passed over the ends of my fingers I would wake up with a start and make a grab for them. If I missed, the whip standing in its socket caught them. I would then pick them up and doze off again, repeating the performance over and over.

The fast, hard drive of many miles out to see the patient usually took enough of the frolic and frivolity out of the horses to make them content to return home no faster than at a brisk trot. But if they changed their gait, or slowed to a walk, I was instantly awake. In that fashion I managed to get considerable sleep in the buggy; but I could never relax completely or sleep as soundly as one does in bed. On a few occasions, however, I was rudely awakened by a wild team tearing madly down the road, or off through the sage brush, but no team ever got away from me or did any particular damage. There was usually plenty of room for the horses to run without running into anything more than big gobs of scenery or great wide open spaces.

When the weather became the hottest near the end of the summer the flood of typhoid reached its height. For two whole weeks during the very hottest part of the summer I did not have my clothes or even my shoes off. No one can fully appreciate what it is like to go that long without having his shoes off in very hot weather without having had the actual experience.

By day and by night I traveled in a cloud of fine gritty dust that settled in my hair and mixed with the perspiration to form a gritty crust over my scalp, with the hairs protruding through it like the quills of a porcupine. I was breathing dust all the time I was in the buggy, and my eyes, nose, mouth, throat, and lungs seemed never entirely free from it. It penetrated my clothing and sifted into my shoes, to mix with the sweat and form a slimy, gritty mess, with slimy mud between my toes. My swollen, blistered feet smarted and burned. I became so light-headed and dizzy that it was an effort to concentrate.

One day as I dozed in the buggy, I dreamed I was in some primitive little European village at vintage time where modern wine presses were unknown. The happy peasants were treading the luscious ripe grapes in a long wooden trough in their bare feet while they sang their vintage songs. A hard jolt when the buggy wheels hit a deep rut woke me, and I suddenly realized that there was something very different from grape juice in my shoes, although it did squash and gurgle a little when I walked. Every muscle in my stiffened body ached and I didn't feel like singing—I'm not much of a singer anyway.

My feet were torturing me so severely that I decided I would take a bath when I got back to town, even if some one died while I was doing it.

Soon after I returned to town that evening, I went to the drug store to get something I needed badly, but I could not remember what I wanted when I got there. I could force my body to move by sheer will power, but my brain refused to function—it was played out. It was natural, I suppose, for the weakest part of me to give out first. While I was trying to remember what I wanted, the kindly old doctor druggist stood puffing on his corn-cob pipe, looking me over.

"You better come with me a moment, doctor," he said. I followed him back of the prescription counter, out a side door, and up an outside stairway that led to the living quarters of his family over the store. He led me into a room with a bed in it.

When I saw that bed I could not resist the temptation to sink down upon it. The old doctor helped me take my shoes off. When he carefully pulled off the socks, rather dilapidated by two weeks of constant wear, the skin over the blisters came off with them. It left raw spots that burned like coals of fire. That was about the last thing I remembered.

The old doctor came and woke me the next day just before noon. I was so stiff and sore that it was painful to move but what a glorious sleep I had had. I had a bath, shave, and a square meal, while I revelled in the thought that no one but the doctor's family knew where I was. The world certainly looked brighter. My feet were so badly swollen that I could not get my shoes on over all the bandages. The good old doctor provided me with a pair of old high-topped lace boots, large enough to go on over the bandages.

With so many desperately sick patients on my hands during the epidemic, I had been worried for fear I was not doing all that could be done for them. The long siege of apprehension and worry, followed by the extreme fatigue, was beginning to make me feel discouraged and pessimistic, but that whole night of sleep in a bed did wonders for me. I threw off my pessimism and began to take stock of the situation.

So far there had not been a death from typhoid. The typhoid patients could be so very low, with life hanging only by a slender thread, for days, and then begin to improve and get well. The first thirty-three patients had passed the danger period and were either well or convalescing. I was beginning to think that the old typhoid demon was not so terrible and voracious after all. Perhaps I was feeling a little too proud of my good luck, for the crash soon came.

A few days after my "big sleep" I went to see a woman whom I had not seen for a week or more. She had been very low with typhoid a month or so before, but at that time was convalescing nicely. She had been nursed throughout her illness by her oldest daughter, a lovely girl of nineteen. In addition to caring for her mother, the girl had done all the housework for the family, consisting of the father and smaller children too young to be of help.

At the time of my last visit to the house about a week before I noticed the girl looked tired, but as she did not complain and my mind was filled with other cases that worried me, I thought little of it. On this afternoon, however, she told me she had a sharp pain in her head and asked me to give her something for it so she could go to a dance that night. She had a new dress to wear and her boy friend was going to take her.

I examined her and found she had a slight fever, a suspicious-looking tongue, and some tenderness in her abdomen. I gave her medicine and ordered her to bed. But she couldn't give up the dance, with her new dress and the boy friend. She fainted on the dance floor and was taken home with a high fever.

I was away in the country that night and did not see

her until morning. When I saw her it gave me a shock. She had vomited and had a hard chill in the night, and her temperature was a hundred and five. The muscles of her back and the back of her neck were tense and tender, drawing her head backward. Her eyes, with pinpoint pupils, were half closed and she was in a semi-stupor. The unmistakable typhoid odor was about her. The diagnosis was very plain—she had typhoid meningitis.

When the surprise and shock at seeing her in such a condition subsided, I was thoroughly aroused and indignant that such a terrible thing should happen to her. She was a lovely girl, and she had worked so hard and taken such wonderful care of her mother.

I got busy immediately with a grim determination to show the old typhoid demon and his whole gang a thing or two. I saw her several times that day and intended to stay at her bedside most of the night, but I was called away to another urgent case in the country.

I went to see her as soon as I returned from the country and did everything I could for her, but it was no use. In forty-eight hours she was dead. I felt terribly guilty for not having sent her to bed when I first noticed she looked tired and was greatly depressed by her death. It was some time before I could entirely shake off my depression and get my confidence back. But there were other cases and I had to keep going.

But that was the only death from typhoid that season, and by the next year, with better housing and sanitary conditions, there were not nearly so many cases. After the second year there were fewer still, an occasional one in town and some scattered over the country.

About the time I was ready to start back home from

a ranch twenty-five miles from town where I had been making a call late one afternoon, Miss Hastings telephoned me and gave me a call to go to a ranch sixty miles southeast of town on a different road. I was only forty miles from the second ranch as the crow flies, but I thought I would have to go back almost to town to get on the road that led there until the rancher at whose house I was told me of a shorter route. About six miles from his place an old unused road branched off and cut across country diagonally to the road I wanted to take. He gave the exact distance to the point where the old road branched off, and described its location and surroundings so accurately that I had no trouble finding it.

There was no moon, but the big luminous desert stars that seemed to hang so low in the heavens gave considerable light and the night was not very dark. The old untraveled cut-off between the two roads ran through wild, rough country, broken by numerous long, low ridges, arroyos and steep canyons, without ranches or other habitation.

I had just gained the top of a slope that brought me out on a little level plateau surrounded on three sides by low ridges when I noticed a fire at the far side of the flat, perhaps a mile away. I thought it a queer place for a camp, as there was no ranch or water near, but accounted for it as probably being an Indian camp, since Indians sometimes were often to be found in out-of-the-way places. As I drew nearer I saw the fire was too large for an Indian camp fire. The Indians always build a small fire they can sit close to and keep warm, while the white man's camp fire is usually so large that he roasts on one side while he freezes on the other.

As I drew nearer, my broncs trotting along briskly, I could see men and horses around the fire. Suddenly I heard the thudding of galloping horses and three riders loomed up out of the darkness in front of me. Before I realized what was going on two of the riders grabbed my horses' bridles while the third dashed up to the side of the buggy and pointed a gun at my head.

"Reach fer tha stars, ole timer!" a deep musical bass voice boomed. I dropped the lines and stuck my hands in the air.

I had a six shooter close at hand, but the fellow had the drop on me before I knew what was happening, and he acted as though he meant business.

"What's up, boys?" I asked in a voice that didn't sound like my own.

No one made a sound, but the man who held the gun on me leaned forward in his saddle, peering at me through the darkness. In a moment the hand that held the gun slowly dropped to his side and the deep bass voice boomed out in a good-natured laugh.

"Oh hell, it's Doc, boys," he said, still laughing.

The men holding the horses' heads relaxed a little and chuckled. I had heard that resonant musical voice somewhere before, but could not remember where, and I could not in the darkness make out the man's features under his wide sombrero.

"It's all right, Doc; just wait a minute," he said, and rode up to the men holding the horses.

They talked in low tones, then the two who had held the horses turned and galloped back to the fire. The man with the deep voice came back to the buggy and began to question me. He wanted to know how I happened to be on that road, where I was going, who was sick, if I had met anyone, etc. By that time I realized that I had unexpectedly happened on a gang of cattle rustlers who had rounded up cattle that did not belong to them and were decorating them with their own brands. After questioning me at some length in a rather friendly manner the deep-voiced rustler said, "Well Doc, go on 'bout yer business an' I'll be gittin' back to mine. Jest be shore an' remember ya ain't seen nothin' or heered nothin' along tha road to-night an' everything'll be jake. I know yo're a smart man an' savvy plenty what's liable to happen to any maverick what talks too damn much. Adios."

He wheeled his horse and galloped back toward the fire and I resumed my journey.

The old road passed within a hundred yards of the fire, which was cleverly located so that it could not be seen from any point on the desert outside of the ridge-surrounded flat. There were six or seven men around the fire, heating their irons to brand a bunch of calves they had rounded up.

I did not mention what I saw that night until many months afterward. It would not have accomplished any good and might have done considerable harm.

On some other occasions I unexpectedly ran onto rustlers at work, but I did not talk and thought I was trusted by all until a little incident happened one night which made me wonder if someone had not reached the conclusion that I knew too much and wanted to get me out of the way.

One evening I was walking down the street to the office just before dusk when Miss Hastings stuck her head out of the telephone office window and shouted at me:

"You better hurry. The girl down at the Couch ranch has taken a sudden turn for the worse and they want you to get down there just as fast as you can."

The girl had been very sick with typhoid fever and I naturally supposed that she was having a hemorrhage. I was soon on my way in the buggy, with the horses going on a good run, when I came to a fork in the Laidlaw road where about two miles of new road had been built. The new road cut off at an angle of about thirty degrees and descended into the Deschutes canyon with a better grade than the old road and crossed the river about two miles above the bridge on the old road.

When I came almost to the place where the new road branched off, I saw in the gathering darkness in front of me a man on a horse standing just a short distance beyond the fork. The horseman was in the middle of the road facing me as though he were waiting for me, and while it seemed a little strange, my first thought was that he had been sent from the ranch to hurry me up. As I came to the fork I pulled the horses up and slowed them to a brisk trot.

As I turned off into the new road the horseman shouted: "Take the old road! Take the old road!"

I thought the strange horseman, whoever he might be, had a lot of gall to tell me what road to take. I thought I knew as much about the roads and where I was going as he did and simply put the horses into a run again, continuing down the new road.

The strange horseman then started to run his horse across the intervening space between the forks of the road in an attempt to head me off, all the while shouting lustily: "Take the old road! Take the old road!"

The space between the forks was filled with sage brush that was tall and thick, and a rough wall of rim-rock jutted up out of the sand to bar his progress. I soon passed on out of sight of him and hurried on to the ranch.

When I arrived, the people were surprised to see me. The girl had passed a good day and no one on the ranch had called me. Thinking I had misunderstood and gone to the wrong place, I called Miss Hastings. She said a man called and told her distinctly to locate me and send me to the Couch Ranch as fast as I could go. She did not recognize his voice.

No one could explain the strange affair and I had too much on my mind to give it much thought. I thought it possible that some of the rustlers I had unintentionally caught stealing stock wanted to get me out of the way for fear I might talk too much. Or one of them, unlucky enough to get shot up a little and afraid to go to town for treatment, or unable to do so, had sent a pal to call and then intercept me and lead me to his hideout. Whatever happened, I never found out who the strange horseman was, or what he wanted.

I did get fictitious calls sometimes, "to attend someone hurt in an accident," and would be intercepted and led off to some out-of-the-way place and told to patch up a rustler who had been shot up in a fracas.

The hard summer's work, with the loss of sleep and the missing of many meals, caused me to lose so much weight that I was pretty thin by the middle of fall. The old time stockmen and ranchers were the most hospitable of people, but they never thought to offer me food except at the regular time for meals. Most of my calls to the ranches were at night, when meals were not being served. Very often I had been without food for many hours, but of course the people at the ranch did not know that and never thought to ask. With the stagnation of business that followed the removal of the big payroll, all the lunch counters and eating places in town closed and there was no place to get a bite to eat except in the dining room of the hotel, which was open only at meal times. Sometimes I went twenty-four hours without a meal. I had so much on my mind, however, that I kept little track of time.

At first I asked housewives for something to eat, but was soon cured of that. I explained that I could not wait for a meal to be cooked, and insisted that they give me just some bread and butter, a sandwich or any cold food they might happen to have, but it was no use. Each time I asked for food when it was not meal time, I invariably had to wait an hour or more while an elaborate meal was prepared. After a few times I quit asking for food and went hungry, many times when I could have eaten a piece of dry bread with relish. But by the middle of fall the typhoid was decreasing. I began to get more sleep and more to eat. I remember that first summer and early fall as a man remembers an indigestion dream after many years.

CHAPTER 7

Teeth Extracted—$1

ONE day late in the fall while I was making a call in a little town twenty-five miles from home, the proprietor of the general store asked me to pull an old snag of a tooth which had been annoying him. I had no extracting forceps with me but found a pair of small pliers in the blacksmith shop. The old snag was so loose I had little difficulty in getting it out.

While working on it a customer came in who was reminded he had a tooth he wanted out, and he knew of others who had teeth they wanted to part with. There was no regular dentist in that section and no traveling dentist had passed through for a long time. Consequently a large crop of undesirable teeth had accumulated. So it was arranged for me to come back a week later, prepared to extract teeth for all and sundry. A notice to that effect was posted in the store and the information was spread all over the country by word of mouth and telephone.

When I arrived on the appointed morning I found thirty or forty people waiting, with more continually arriving. The lack of a dental chair was overcome by the use of two ordinary straight-backed kitchen chairs, placed in the center of the floor, one behind the other.

The patient sat in the foremost chair while I stood just to his right and behind him. I placed my left foot on the

89

seat of the rear chair and the patient leaned back a little and laid his head on my left knee. I then put my left arm around his head and grasped his lower jaw with my left hand. This gave me a strangle hold on his head and left my strong right hand and arm free to handle the forceps and do the dirty work.

Those tough old pioneers never thought of having an anaesthetic to have a tooth pulled. They were accustomed to enduring pain without an anaesthetic and would have thought it sissified to have one. The presence of a crowd was also a help, for no one wanted his neighbor to see him shrink from a little pain.

The extracting began at about nine o'clock and continued until noon, when the crowd adjourned to the hotel for lunch. After an hour of rest and refreshment, the extracting resumed and continued until late in the afternoon. There was a crowd of spectators watching the performance at all times and they contributed to the entertainment by their jibes and witty remarks, both about my technique and the reaction of the victims. Some time in the forenoon an old buck Indian joined the crowd and stood unobtrusively and silently on its outer edge.

When I came back after lunch he was seated on a box directly in front of the dental chair and I noticed his left jaw was swollen. He watched with stoic interest and changeless expression until I happened to pull a lower left second molar for a patient. When I dropped the tooth into a receptacle on the floor he picked it up, examining it closely.

"Skookum, skookum," he grunted, "me ketchum same like him," and looked at me inquiringly.

I motioned him to the chair and he sat down. His gums

were swollen and oozing a little pus. I thought the second molar was ulcerated but to make sure and not pull the wrong tooth I tapped it lightly with an artery forceps. The old boy let out a war-whoop, leaped from the chair and did a war-dance, holding his jaw with both hands. I felt reasonably sure then that I had spotted the right tooth.

"Hyu Skookum, goddam you no hit 'em, drag 'em!" he reproached me, then went through the pantomime of pulling the tooth. I got him back in the chair as soon as possible for I knew it must be hurting terribly. There must have been lots of sand in the pemmican he had been eating throughout his many years for his teeth were badly worn down. That condition, and the swollen gums, prevented me from getting a sufficient hold with the forceps and they slipped off with the first vigorous yank. He let out another war-whoop, grabbed my arm and fell to the floor. There he rolled, holding his face and emitting mighty groans and grunts.

I hurriedly called for volunteers to assist me. With one man sitting on his legs and two holding each arm I got down on the floor on my knees with one knee on his chest. That time I got a good hold with the forceps and yanked the tooth out. I held the tooth up where the old boy could get a good look at it and his groans ceased. He rose from the floor slowly, holding his jaw, and stalked out of the store with majestic deliberation, without a word, without paying the customary dollar for the extraction. I let him go as I figured he got the worst of the tussle.

The extracting continued until late in the afternoon. I do not know how many people attended that hilarious party, or how many teeth I pulled, but I doubt if there are many dentists who have pulled as many teeth in a single day.

Today that would be crude dentistry, but the old pioneers thought they were fortunate to have someone available with a strong right arm and a set of extracting forceps. The only means of getting rid of a bad tooth when there was no dentist available was to have the blacksmith take a punch and hammer and knock the tooth out.

I had a complete set of extracting forceps which had belonged to my father at a time when all general practitioners pulled teeth. A local anaesthetic was rarely if ever used; but if a patient had a large number of teeth extracted at one time, I usually gave him a general anaesthetic. Before the country was settled and supplied with dentists, extracting teeth was one of my regular duties.

CHAPTER 8

Accidents and Indians

THE wild range horses caused many an accident. One day the telephone rang and a man's voice came over the wire:

"Hello Doc! This is George Hays out at the half-way stage station. Say, Doc—are you there Doc?—say, Hank Bradley the stage driver's got a broken leg an' he wants ya to meet the stage whin he gits to the barn an' fix it up fer 'im.

"Whin he was jest about ready to pull out 'a here he noticed one of his tugs on the off-wheel hoss was unhooked. Whin he stepped up behin' tha hoss to hook it up agin the damn bastard cut loose an' kicked the hell outen him an' broke his leg plumb in two. I was a goin' to drive in fer 'im but he wouldn' have it. He clumb up to the seat hisself an' fished a quart out a the boot an' took a few jolts an' beat it out a here like a bat out a hell. Ya want a be lookin' fer 'm."

The stage station was about eighteen miles out, two hours' drive, but I heeded George's warning and started for the barn in what I thought was ample time.

Before I reached the barn, however, I heard the thunder of running hoofs, the explosions of the driver's whip and the rattle and rumble of wheels. The old dust-covered stage lurched into view, rocking and swaying down the road, the horses on the run.

Imposing and majestic on the driver's seat sat Hank Bradley, his wide sombrero cocked at a rakish angle, his sound foot planted on the brake to hold the stage back off the running horses.

His broken leg hung dangling outside of the stage boot, the portion below the fracture swinging in all directions with the swaying of the stage. When Hank saw the crowd assembled to see the stage come in, he raised the leg to a horizontal position, the portion below the fracture hanging down at an angle of forty-five degrees, so all might see it was broken and take notice of his contempt for such a triviality.

With screeching brakes and a yank on the reins Hank brought the stage to an abrupt stop, tossed the reins down to the hostlers, pulled a half empty quart bottle out of the boot of the stage and took a man-sized swig.

Both bones of the leg were broken in a compound fracture, the ends of the bones protruding through the skin, but Hank thought I should be able to splint it up so he could go on to the end of his run, ninety miles farther. He had consumed enough whiskey to make him argumentative and I had some difficulty in persuading him to go to bed in the hotel.

The leg was put in a fracture box until the flesh wounds had healed; then a plaster cast was put on and he was allowed to be up on crutches. Three days later he got into a fight in a saloon and injured the leg again. He was very meek and penitent after that, but I did not trust him and took his crutches away until it was safe for him to be up.

The stage station where Hank's leg was broken seemed

to be an unlucky place; several men were injured by horses there. But I remember Bill Hawkins' case in particular.

Bill, a typical Eastern Oregon Bunch Grasser, was born and grew to young manhood on the vast sage brush plateau east of the Cascade Mountains. Living much out of doors in that healthful climate, he acquired about the same kind and amount of vitality as that possessed by a grizzly bear. He was not yet thirty when I first knew him.

Bill's schooling must have been limited, for when he was still a lad in his teens he drove a sixteen-horse freight outfit for his uncle, hauling freight from The Dalles on the Columbia to Silver Lake and points two hundred and fifty miles south.

I had a liking for Bill. He was a good worker and always paid his debts; he was fond of his horses and kind to them; and he was always good-natured and accommodating. He had one failing, however; when he got liquored up he had a passion for fighting and no ordinary man could lick him. If he was licked he wouldn't know it but would keep right on fighting unless he was knocked out; and he was so tough no ordinary man could knock him out, or pummel him into submission. Between freighting seasons he worked at odd jobs, driving stage, busting broncos or punching cattle.

One bitter cold morning Bill was kicked by a horse out at the same stage station where Hank Bradley had his leg broken.

The sharp-shod toe calk of the horse's shoe struck him at the top of his forehead, just at the edge of his long hair, stripping a three-inch piece of scalp clean from the skull from the forehead to the back of his head. Bill replaced the strip of scalp covered with long hair and tied his red bandanna handkerchief tightly down over it and under his chin.

The bandanna pressed the torn flap of scalp and a lot of long hair down into the wound so tightly that it helped control the bleeding, and the bitter cold weather quickly froze the blood; otherwise the hemorrhage would have been serious.

Bill saddled his bronc and rode the eighteen miles to town in quick time, the blood running down over his eyes so he could scarcely see and freezing in such big clots and cakes all over his face that I did not know him when he walked into the office. But when he spoke in his droll way I recognized his resonant voice.

"Sew up this goddam fool head 'o mine, Doc, 'fore all them damn little brains 'o mine falls out," he said. "I ain't got enough of 'em now, or I'd had sense enough to 'a spoke to that goddam onry cayuse 'fore I went an' walked up behind 'im. I guess I'm a lucky bastard at that though; if he'd 'a hit me somewheres besides my damn fool head it might 'a hurt me."

Bill sat bolt upright in a chair while I cleaned the mess, shaved his head and took about thirty stitches in his scalp. All the while he was chatting away in his friendly style, without a flinch or even a grunt. He told me about some of the good fights he had had since I saw him last, particularly about a fight he had in a saloon in another town called "The Bucket of Blood." This fight was with a sheep herder who was Basque and Indian. The vile names he called that breed—whew! He showed me the scar where the breed stabbed him with a knife before he could land the wallop that broke the breed's jaw and knocked him cold.

With all of his long hair shaved off, I was afraid Bill would take cold, as he could not get his sombrero on over all the bandages and dressings. I wanted him to stay in the hotel a day or two, the weather being near zero, but he left for a ranch forty-five miles away where he had promised to help round up some cattle on the snow-covered range and drive them into the feed lots; and he intended to keep his word "even if Hell froze over."

Bill's idea of a vacation was to have a good spree, and no spree was of much account unless there was a good fight somewhere in it.

On one occasion Bill came to town for a vacation and celebration when the town was quiet and he could find no one around the saloons who craved a fight with him, so he betook himself down to the sporting houses in his quest for amusement.

When the girls in the first house Bill came to saw he was on a rampage, they locked the doors to keep him out. That so offended his dignity that he kicked the door down and went in anyway. He scattered the furniture around the place and rearranged it to suit his artistic taste, then turned the upright piano upside down in the parlor.

When the girls in the second house heard Bill was coming to see them, they fled uptown to take refuge in the hotel. That offended him still more, and he decided he would go to the hotel and chase the girls back home. The hotel proprietor objected to Bill's playfulness and called the city marshal to stop him.

The city marshal at that time was a soft-spoken, big-fisted, husky old Scot by the name of Tom McDuff. Tom had spent many years in the service of the famous Northwest Mounted Police, and had retired, only to find that life held little interest for him unless he could be a peace officer of some kind. When the office of city marshal was offered he accepted it.

Tom believed in a wide open town. He had never known any other kind and did not arrest anybody for getting drunk unless he created too big a disturbance. But when Tom did decide to make an arrest he did it in a businesslike manner and with few words; and if it were a bad man he was after, he upheld the tradition of the Mounties. He always got his man.

When old Tom came up to Bill and told him he was under arrest, Bill started to fight. Tom neatly side-stepped a vicious swing at his jaw and gave Bill a mighty wallop on the head with the butt of his big heavy Colt six-shooter.

Bill hit the plank side-walk like a steer that had been shot through the brain, but he was up fighting in a jiffy. Tom repeated the performance twice more and Bill was a little slow in getting up the third time, and appeared to be a little groggy, with some of the fight taken out of him. But he had a sheepish grin on his weather-bronzed face, just as though he and Tom had been playing a little game of some kind.

"Well, Tom, ya did that purty nice fer an old feller—ya sure got a hard mitt," he drawled in his comical way, "but ya don't need ta hit me again. I'll go 'long with ya if ya ain't too high toned ta be walkin' down the street with me."

With Tom's big fist gripping Bill's coat collar, they

marched off down the street until Bill's head cleared a little and he quickly slipped out of his coat and outran
Tom. They were good friends and Tom did not want to
shoot, so he had to let Bill get away. Bill got to his saddle-
horse and rode away to another town to continue his celebration. Tom sent him word to come back and surrender
or he would swear out a warrant charging him with re-
sisting arrest.

When Bill had sobered up a little he came back and
surrendered, with profuse apologies and mock formality.

"I didn't mean no harm, Tom," he explained, "I was
jest tryin' to have a little fun in this here goddam dead
town where nothin' never happens an' I got the wrong
kind 'a booze. Ya know some of this here booze has got
music an' singin' in it, an' some of it has got gamblin' an'
women in it, and some of it is jest full of fightin' an'
hellin' around, an' that's the kind that there goddam onry
bartender give me. He orta knowed better. It wasn't my
fault."

Bill promised to pay for the property damage to the
sporting house and turn the piano right side up again and
be more careful of the variety of whiskey he drank in the
future. Tom accepted Bill's apologies. They shook hands
on Bill's good resolutions and the incident was closed.

"Be after lavin' tha crazy American whuskie alone, me
young laddie," Tom admonished, "It'll be gittin' ye shot
'stead 'a only half shot if ye don't." Tom never touched
anything but old imported Scotch.

But Bill lived a charmed life as far as bullets were concerned—he was shot at but never hit.

Bill formed a close friendship with a very young but
widely traveled buckaroo recently arrived from Texas

who had made a hasty trip to Oregon for his health. He failed to state whether it was Texas mosquitoes, rangers or sheriffs that made Texas so unhealthful for him, but he became a great aid and comfort to Bill on his periodic sprees.

After drinking all of one afternoon, the two buckaroos went into the "Pass Time Resort" in the evening, just as the night bartender, who happened to be a Frenchman, came on shift.

Informed of the bartender's nationality, the cosmopolite young Texan remarked that the French people ate frogs. He had actually seen them do it in the French Restaurants in New Orleans when he happened to go there with train loads of cattle from Western Texas. That information disturbed Bill's equanimity somewhat as he considered anyone who would eat a frog to be lower than a Piute Injun, and he had absolutely no use for a Piute. But Bill remembered his good resolutions and managed to contain himself until the Frenchman tried to short change the boys, or at least Bill thought he did.

That started a first-class ruckus and the boys threw their glasses and everything else at hand at the mirror in the back bar. When the Frenchman ducked under the bar for his gun, Bill crowned him with an inverted cuspidor. The boys ran into the street for rocks to throw and the irate Frenchman followed to the door with his gun.

He attempted to shoot Bill in the leg and put him out of commission so he would have a more even chance with the Texan, but the street was so dark on the far side he could not see Bill well. Just as Bill stooped to pick up a rock at his feet, the Frenchman fired and the bullet knocked the rock out of his hand. Bill thought the Frenchman had intentionally shot the rock out of his hand and decided he was a good sport to shoot the rock instead of him; also that he was a crack shot. A good sport himself, Bill admired sportsmanship in others; he had, too, a high regard for a crack shot. He decided this Frenchman was a pretty good fellow, even if he did eat frogs.

Hearing the shot, old Tom McDuff appeared on the scene and took the Frenchman's gun away from him (it was supposed to be a violation of city ordinances to discharge firearms within the city limits). Tom thought Bill had had enough drinks for the time being and escorted him to my office to have the particles shattered from the rock by the bullet picked out of his hand. Tom's appearance at the right moment brought the ruckus to a harmless ending.

That was about as near as I ever came to treating Bill for a gun-shot wound. He was shot at many times, but never hit. I did have gun-shot wounds to treat, however, when it so happened that a doctor was needed instead of the undertaker.

One night that fall the telephone gave an ominous jingle just at dark and I recognized the voice of a deputy sheriff as it came over the wire.

"Hello, Doc, can you go up to Bogue's store right away? There's been a gun-fight between some sheepmen and Injuns near there, an' from what I hear some of 'em is pretty badly shot up." Bogue's store was a general store and post-office, thirty-two miles up the river south of town, with a blacksmith shop and a few houses near it.

The night was about the blackest one I ever saw and it was so dark I could not see much of it. The road there ran through the pine timber nearly all the way, and it was so dark in the timber I could not even see the horses I was driving. It was rather an odd sensation to hold one end of the reins and not be able to see what was at the other end.

I met the incoming mail stage about ten miles out and stopped to get information about the shooting. The driver had nailed a six-foot length of board on the front of the stage, between the boot and the driver's seat, that had a kerosene lantern with a reflector fastened on each end, so the light was thrown on the horses and road ahead. The only passenger was a salesman from the east, making his first trip in the wild and woolly west. Sickened and nervous from what he had seen at the place of the shooting, he had become jittery listening to the tall tales of the driver about gun-fights, stage holdups and range wars.

"I wouldn't have your job for all the money in Oregon," he sang out to me through the darkness as I drove on.

Two sheepmen, trailing their sheep from the summer range in the mountains to the home ranches, passed a camp of Warm Spring Indians on the way from the fall deer hunt to the reservation. The white men gave the Indian bucks whiskey and engaged them in a horse trade which ended in a fight at a point some distance from the camp.

When I arrived at Bogue's store about daylight, I found two badly injured bucks lying in an open shed back of the store.

One buck, who was perhaps fifty, was unconscious with a fractured skull. A bruise on the right side of his head, and another across his right forearm, indicated that he had thrown up his arm to ward off the blow which had broken the stock of the rifle and knocked him down on his face. While he was still lying prone on the ground, his opponent, grasping the stockless gun by the muzzle, struck him in the center of the back of the head in such a way that the hammer of the gun was driven into the skull, making an indented fracture. A wad of his coarse black hair was driven down into the fracture and wedged so tightly that it could not be pulled out.

The other buck, who was perhaps forty, had been shot through the left lung with a 30-30 soft-nosed bullet. The bullet entered just over the heart and split into two fragments, both of which penetrated the lung and shoulder blade and came out of his back, making holes about the size of a half dollar, three inches apart.

The lacerated lung had bled profusely and was still bleeding when I arrived. The buck was conscious, but so weak from the loss of blood he could not speak above a whisper.

The sheepmen, who were the aggressors, were not seriously hurt and were nowhere about.

The deputy and men about the store thought both bucks would die and did not try to do anything for them. Had the squaws in the camp been notified, they would have given the wounded bucks good care until I arrived.

The wounded Indians had been left lying in an old shed, entirely open on one side, without blankets or a fire to keep them warm; and the night was chilly. There was no indication that they had even been given water; and the buck that had bled so much must have had a raging thirst. Such callous neglect thoroughly aroused my indignation, but I managed to hold my tongue until I suggested that the Indians be brought into the store, where it was warmer, and I could give them better attention.

"What's the use, Doc? Why not let 'em die in peace

where they're at? They'll be good Injuns when they're dead Injuns," the deputy said with a grin.

That was too much for my pent up wrath—I exploded. While I was still telling the deputy and others what I thought of them, with some of their ancestors thrown in, some of the men present slipped out and brought the bucks into the store.

I felt sorry for the poor neglected devils and wanted at least to make them as comfortable as possible, even if it were impossible to save their lives. I knew their squaws and families would suffer just as much grief if they died as anybody else does who loses a loved one.

The hemorrhage from the lacerated lung was stopped by packing the wounds with narrow strips of iodoform gauze, a yard long. The buck was then given stimulants, fluid and nourishment. After he got warm and comfortable he was able to talk.

After the older buck had been ministered to for a time he became conscious and complained of a terrible headache.

The Indians in the camp two or three miles away had been notified of the shooting and moved their camp near the store where they could take care of their wounded.

The deputy sheriff had instructions to arrest all parties engaged in the fight and bring them to the county seat at once. I was still provoked at him for his callous neglect and lack of sympathy and forbade him to move or even touch the Indians for twenty-four hours, until they had had time to recover from their shock.

The following morning the wounded bucks were placed in a wagon on a bed of loose hay and brought the thirty-two miles to Bend. The entire camp of three or four families followed, with the outfit on pack ponies, and went into camp at the edge of town. The next morning when I went to their camp a friend went with me and took some kodak pictures of the shot Indian while I was dressing his wounds.

All the squaws of the camp gathered in the tepee of the shot buck, jabbering away in Injun jargon. When I started carefully pulling the long strips of gauze out of the bullet holes in his back there was a sudden silence followed by grunts and exclamations of surprise, but the wounded buck did not flinch or make a sound.

It was necessary to trephine the skull of the older buck and remove a round piece of bone, the size of a quarter, in order to remove the tuft of hair from the fracture.

The next day the Indians were taken to the county seat where they were arraigned in court along with the sheepmen. If I remember correctly, the sheepmen were fined twenty-five dollars for giving liquor to the Indians. If one of the Indians should have been so careless as to die from his injuries, the sheepmen, who were the aggressors in the fight, might have been given several days in jail.

Both of the Indians recovered, and several months later I received a letter from the Indian who was shot. He stated that his shoulder was crippled but that he was able to use an axe some.

CHAPTER 9

Prostitution on the Frontier

WITH the first cold nights of fall my problems decreased.
The flies disappeared. Typhoid and dysentery cases
dropped off. I began to take it a little easier.

But construction work had stopped, too, and there
was no payroll. Building operations came to a standstill.
The two small saw mills shut down for the winter. The
little town was quiet and still, drawing into itself. Money
that had been so plentiful became scarce. My collections suffered accordingly.

There were idle men loafing around with nothing to
do but gossip or go hunting. Most of the women had
little to occupy them beyond gossiping. Much of this
tale-tattling was friendly and harmless; occasionally it
was mischievous; but a lot of it was malicious and down-
right vicious.

I had never lived in so small a town before, or in one
where gossip was so rife, nor had I been in contact with
people given to gossip. Consequently it was both astonishing and annoying to me. I tried to ignore it but I do not
think I succeeded very well as it never ceased to annoy
me, and I grew to despise the malicious gossiper.

I soon found I had to be very careful not to give any
information about a patient as I was sure to be mis-

quoted by some busybody who liked to give a story a little coloring.

If a married woman happened to have a miscarriage, the tale bearers were sure to accuse her of bringing it about herself. I made it a rule not to tell anyone what the patient was suffering from when I attended any woman with a miscarriage, much to the displeasure of the tattlers.

One day when I was leaving the home of a woman who was seriously ill from the effects of a miscarriage, I noticed her neighbor had planted herself at her front gate to intercept me. She was one of the worst gossips in town. As I came up to her she blurted, "Now doctor I want you to tell me exactly what is the matter with Mrs. ——."

"Why, haven't you heard the news?" I asked in feigned surprise, "Mrs. —— has been very sick for the past two days," and walked on past her without another word. She gave me a dirty look, stuck her nose in the air and marched into the house. She was so mad at me she spent her time saying mean things about me, thus sparing her sick neighbor.

One of the most accomplished of the venomous gossips was a middle-aged married woman who believed she possessed more than ordinary ability and aptitude for nursing. It had been her girlhood ambition to be a nurse, but cruel circumstances had prevented it. After marrying late in life, she sought to compensate her thwarted ambition by volunteering her services to sick friends and neighbors.

She swelled with pride when permitted to nurse a sick friend and took special pains to display her profound knowledge to both patient and doctor. She would explain in detail just how some doctor she had nursed under would treat the case at hand and give me suggestions for treatment. She annoyed me in many ways, but I managed to hold my peace.

Her greatest delight lay in telling how she had nursed her three-and-a-half-year-old daughter through an attack of pneumonia after several doctors had given her up. She would go on and on, telling why the little darling had been so delicate ever since, why she would even now soon die if she had an ordinary mother to care for her who lacked her own wonderful ability.

One afternoon she called me frantically to come in haste to see the child, who was suffering with some terrible and mysterious malady that even she herself could not diagnose.

"I had just given the little angel her bath and set her down very gently in her crib when she suddenly cried out with a terrible pain right in her little bottom," the frantic mother said. "The pain is so severe and it came on so suddenly I'm sure something terrible is the matter. She never had a pain in her bottom before. I know it's something very serious—do hurry doctor—she's crying so."

I hurried. When I came within a block or two of the house I heard a noise that convinced me there was nothing wrong with the little angel's lungs. Neighbor women were running to the house from all directions.

Entering I found myself in the midst of a crowd of excited women. Some of them were listening breathlessly to the mother's dramatic recital of the tragedy. Others were frantically running circles around the child's crib, instilling more excitement into her. Meanwhile, the child sat in her crib squalling at the top of her voice.

The mother rushed up to me and began telling me her

story. I walked quietly over to the crib and picked the little thing up. As I held her in my arms I ran my hand over her bottom. That had a soothing effect. Another caress or two and the squalling stopped. The women all looked surprised and slightly startled.

Looking down into the crib, I noticed a bulge, or what would medically be termed a protuberance, in the blanket spread over the bottom of the crib in the exact spot where the little angel's little bottom had been reposing. I felt after the bulge and discovered a hard object underneath the blanket. Picking up the blanket, I found an empty mucilago bottle.

While the mother's face grew red, I ventured the shrewd deduction that the terrible pain her angel had suffered was probably owing to the fact that she had been sitting on the bottle. One inconsiderate female tittered and the mother's face turned crimson. Another whispered in her neighbor's ear, and that clownish female was so indelicate as to break out in loud and unbecoming laughter while the mother's embarrassment took on a decided tinge of anger.

I tried to soothe her with the assurance that the bottle had done no harm. But it was a terrible blow. The exciting party began to break up as the neighbor women left for home. But the mother's prestige as a nurse, I am afraid, disappeared with them.

During the months the town was quiet many of the people had little to do but interest themselves in the business and personal affairs of others. A student of human nature and life in a small frontier town would have found the situation interesting. There was little going on to set one day apart from the others. There were no movies in those early days, and except for church services on Sundays and an occasional dance, there was no evening entertainment outside of the saloons and gambling joints. The high light of the day's events was the arrival of the mail stage each evening, but that was uncertain in the worst weather of the winter.

At one time, after a blizzard and heavy snow storm, the roads to the north were blocked with snow so the stages could not get through, and for twenty-one days no mail came in or went out of town.

Occasionally a thirsty bunch of buckaroos who had just drawn a few months' wages came in to celebrate and liven things up. There might be a poker game lasting a few days, or until the local gamblers had stripped the boys, but there was sure to be a good spree and probably a rattling good fist fight somewhere in it to furnish a little excitement for the loafers.

Occasionally bands of wild range horses were driven through on the way to outside markets. Some of the best in the band would often be bought by local people; that furnished a little diversion.

When the horses were saddled and ridden for the first time, the populace was treated to a riding and bucking exhibition, either on the main street or in the corral by the livery stable. Although a bucking horse was a common sight, the riding of a wild horse for the first time never failed to draw a crowd.

During the dull days the Commercial Club and Bend boosters never lost their faith in the future of the town and were always talking and planning for the big boom that would be sure to come with the advent of the new railroad. When there was nothing else to do everyone talked railroad.

The one Protestant church building in town was owned by the Baptists but used by all denominations.

The only resident minister seemed unable to draw a congregation on Sunday evenings and after resorting to various schemes to fill his pews he would ask different ones of the citizens to talk on Sunday evenings on any subject. The first person to accept the invitation was an old veteran of the Civil War.

He was one of the first settlers, the handy man about town, noted for his industry, his fluent and original profanity and his love of talking about the Civil War. He was well liked and a fair-sized crowd turned out to hear him.

The Vet was a little awkward and embarrassed when he stepped into the pulpit, but he had a strong voice and a forceful delivery, and plunged boldly into his story.

During the first part of his talk the old boy remembered he was in the house of the Lord and, with considerable effort, managed to avoid profanity. But as he progressed he lost his caution and became intensely interested in his story. Captured by the Confederates and sent to Andersonville, he had been the only one entering the prison at the time to come out alive. The fire of battle flashed from his eyes as he continued:

"My company cut down some trees in some woods and made some breast works, and we was behind them breast works a pourin' lead into them Jonnies ta beat hell, an' afore I knowed it them goddam Jonnies come a chargin' up through them woods hell-bent-fur-'lection an' jumped over them breast works all around me. One goddam big

Jonnie stuck his baynet at my guts an' says, 'Surrender ya Yankie son-of-a-bitch or I'll blow ya all ta hell.' "

The good sisters of the congregation were greatly shocked, but the men laughed and applauded. The old Vet then realized he had used profanity in the house of the Lord and retired in disorder. The minister did not ask any more laymen to address the congregation.

I never realized how much music meant to me until I had been without it a few months. There were very few pianos in town and a few musicians; aside from the pianos, there was no music except that furnished by the old-fashioned phonographs which sounded terrible. But after being without any music, even the old phonographs were better than nothing.

I had played clarinet during my college days and still had my clarinet. One evening when I actually had no calls to make for a few hours, I unpacked the old clarinet and started playing in the office. The noise attracted a few people from the street and a small crowd gathered in the office. We discovered that there were several musicians in the group and plans were started to organize a band.

A date was set for the first rehearsal and any musicians in town invited to attend. About thirty of us musicians and would-be musicians came to the meeting. I was chosen director. The organization of the band was completed, regular rehearsals were held, and the band gave a few dances to which the public was invited and an admission charged.

The band was just about the sort of aggregation one would expect to find in a town of that size. I was too busy to attend rehearsals regularly and did not know anything about directing, but a first-class cornet player who was a better director than I came to town and made a creditable organization of it.

I was away in the country on calls so much of the time that I was not in close contact with the gossip and little incidents that made life in the little town during its quiescent period interesting. The baby cases were numerous and frequent, with usually two or three neighbor women present at the party, and they kept me posted on all the latest scandal, gossip, and exciting new railroad rumors.

An advertisement ran in the local newspapers for several weeks which stated that Dr. ——, the renowned European specialist, would be at the hotel in the county seat for a week for the benefit and convenience of all who wished to consult him. A patient of mine went to consult him and was swindled out of two hundred and fifty dollars.

The patient was a man sixty-two years old, well preserved and fairly sound physically, except for infected tonsils with which he refused to part. He was of the hypochondriac order, with a strong aversion to work, but managed to keep the other members of his family at work supporting him. He suffered with back aches and pains in his legs from his infected tonsils but because of the back ache he was sure he had "kidney trouble" and feared he would die of Bright's disease.

I assured him there was nothing wrong with his kidneys and promised him that if he would have his tonsils out and go to work he would be all right. He did not agree with my diagnosis and went to see the "renowned specialist."

The quack promptly agreed with his diagnosis of "kidney trouble" but told him that, instead of having Bright's disease, he had something worse, a rare ailment that ordinary doctors probably knew nothing about. To prove his diagnosis was correct he would give the patient some medicine which would make the urine blue should he have this rare disease. He promised to cure him for two hundred and fifty dollars, but the patient had only a hundred with him.

The beneficent specialist would fix all that. He could not bear to see anyone die of this rare disease he alone could cure. He sent his assistant home with the patient while he raised the other one hundred and fifty. As soon as the money was paid he would be given the medicine and the cure would start at once.

The money was paid and the assistant gave him some pills to take at bed time.

When the old boy woke in the morning his urine was as blue as the sky and he was astonished and delighted. He collected some of the blue urine in an old tomato can so he could show it to anyone who might be skeptical. With his cane in one hand and the can of blue urine in the other, he came parading down the street with the air of a man who had just discovered a rich gold strike. He stopped everyone he met, both friend and stranger, told his story and exhibited the marvel. It was some time before he could be convinced he was the victim of a fraud, but by that time the "renowned specialist" had skipped out and nothing could be done about it. The quack had given him pills with a methylene blue dye in them. They would make any person's urine blue.

Although gossip seemed to be the principal delight and

occupation of many of the women, especially those of the reform group and those within the fold of the redeemed, the women did not have a monopoly on the gossip by any means. Probably the busiest and most persistent gossip of those supposed to belong to the male gender was one who the wags about town dubbed the "he virgin." He did not chew, smoke, drink, swear or appear to have a single human appetite or impulse.

He was of the most dogmatic religious belief and circumspect morals, the self-appointed censor of the habits of those who did not belong to his own church. Those within the fold of his own denomination, he believed, could do no wrong. The extreme repressions he had practiced, and his belief that everything pertaining to sex was sinful and immoral, had made him one of the most vulgar minded men I ever met. He was possessed of a remarkable faculty, like a sixth sense, which immediately notified him when a new sporting girl came to town. Before anyone else knew of her presence, the old boy knew who she was, where she came from and all about her, and immediately appeared before the mayor with the demand that she be run out of town.

With the sporting girls away during the dull period, except for an occasional transient, the "he virgin" declared he would keep them out. When the big lumber companies began buying up all the small tracts of timber more money was put in circulation and there was a prospect of business revival. An enterprising madam then came to town with the intention of opening a first-class sporting house, but the "he virgin" and his little band of reformers created strong opposition to her. Instead of opening a house in town, the madam went just across the line outside the city limits and opened a rather pretentious establishment on the same side of town the old boy lived on. It was a large two-story house but without modern conveniences or plumbing.

The "he virgin" was very mad about that and declared he would put the place out of business by fair means or foul. It was his plan to spy on the place and list the names of all men who entered there, then threaten them with exposure unless they compelled the madam to close the place and leave town. He slept in the day-time and spied on the place at night.

One dark foggy night, when he was compelled to take a position close to the house in order to identify all who entered, he hid behind a large clump of sage brush directly beneath the open window of a second-story bedroom.

Suddenly and unexpectedly a dashing torrent descended on him from above and a vile and pungent odor told his olfactory nerves, unmistakably, that the girl in the room above had emptied the slop jar which had been reposing under her bed for an unknown period. Whether the girl saw him and doused him intentionally or merely thought the jar should be emptied no one but the girl knows; but in either event she made a perfect shot. Some of the vile stuff went inside his coat collar and down his neck and back.

He thought every sporting girl had some venereal disease. His ideas of what venereal diseases were like were vague, but he had a holy horror of them all and was terribly afraid he had become infected from the contents of the jar. Mad as a wet hen and thoroughly frightened, he rushed home, took a bath, changed his clothes, then hurried uptown and got me out of bed.

Gesticulating wildly, he spluttered and squawked so in his angry, high pitched, squeally voice, as he told me he had been exposed to a venereal disease and wanted me to disinfect him, that I could not understand all he said. I could not believe any girl would get close enough to him to seduce him, in the first place, and in the second place, I doubted his ability to negotiate a real exposure. I told him I would have to know the nature of the exposure to know what steps to take to disinfect him. Then he related the whole misfortune in all its sordid details. His wild gesticulating palaver was the most comical exhibition of histrionic fireworks I ever witnessed, and I laughed until out of breath, much to his disgust.

Since he came to me as a patient, I treated his misfortune as a professional secret and did not tell anyone, but he must have told it himself. The story leaked out and came to the ears of the madam of the house. She stationed a guard to watch at night and prevent further spying. The next time the foxy old sleuth went back to spy, the guard saw him and would have handled him rather roughly, I am afraid, had he been able to catch the old boy; but he showed surprising speed and outran the guard. He was afraid to go back after that and the spying ceased.

I had soon discovered, as time went on, that there was one phase of the sporting-house question that was of vital importance to me that the reformers and general public knew nothing about. When there were no sporting houses running I was frequently consulted by young unmarried girls who were "in trouble" and wanted me to do an abortion. When the houses were running, that sort of thing rarely happened, and I was truly thankful, for the responsibility of dealing properly with those cases caused me no end of grief and worry.

I always felt sorry for the unfortunate girls, and down in the bottom of my heart wanted to help them, but it was illegal to do an abortion and contrary to medical ethics.

The first girl to come to me "in trouble" was a bright, attractive high-school girl just past eighteen, the oldest daughter of prominent citizens. Her father was to all appearances well-to-do but not engaged in any business. He was active in one of the churches, a strict moralist, a rabid prohibitionist, and took a prominent part in the activities of the reform group. He spent most of his time loafing around the stores gossiping, talking prohibition and complaining about the morals of the town.

The girl's mother was active in church work and the W.C.T.U., and kept a sharp eye on her daughters. She did not allow them to dance, play cards, or keep company with the boys, and compelled them to attend church regularly.

The boy in the case was several years older than the girl, and the son of well-to-do parents. He was good looking, dressed well, was usually idle, and was quite a beau among the girls. He had been in a similar scrape before. The girl's parents objected to him because his religion differed from theirs and he did not have a very good reputation. They did not allow the girl to invite him into the house. He went to her church Sunday evenings and walked home with her, and waited on the street afternoons to walk home from school with her. He was her first real beau and she was madly in love with him.

When the girl, who had always been lively and vivacious, suddenly became depressed, lost her appetite and had headaches, her mother sent her to the office. I found out she was pregnant. She was terrified at the thought of her parents' discovering the fact. I promised not to tell until we could determine what to do. I told her to send the boy up to me.

The next day he came and I tried to get him to marry her, but he refused. He had many excuses: He did not love her. To him the affair was just another adventure. He said it probably would not have happened had there been sporting houses running. He laid a stack of twenty dollar gold pieces on the desk and begged me to do an abortion.

The girl came back the following day and I had a long talk with her. Her mother had never instructed her in the things every girl should know. On a few occasions when she had asked her mother frank questions she had been given evasive answers, or been told that nice girls did not talk about such things. I was surprised to find how little she knew about sexual problems. She was so much in love with the boy that she had trusted him completely, hardly realizing what it was all about.

I made the mistake of threatening to tell the girl's father when the boy refused to marry her. He got scared, gave the girl money to go to Portland for an abortion, then skipped out.

When the wretched girl found out the boy did not love her and had decamped leaving her to face the situation alone, she was heartbroken; then her mother discovered what was the matter with her. Then, of course, her father

heard of it and put on a real exhibition. He upbraided
and abused her terribly, told her to get out of his house
and stay out, that he never wanted to see her "sinful face"
again. He was a real Christian gentleman and could not
possibly stand the disgrace of living under the same roof
with one so sinful as his unfortunate daughter. Such a
thing would deprive him of the delight and satisfaction
of harping about the morals of others; people might
whisper behind his back when he delivered tirades about
the morals of the town. The mother had some sympathy
for the poor girl and tried to intercede with the irate
father, but it was of no use; the girl had to go at once.
Utterly crushed and heartbroken, she came to the office
and told me what had happened. I gave her a letter to
a doctor friend of mine in Portland and she fled to the
city on the first stage.

The doctor helped her to gain admission to a Florence
Crittenden home there, and in due time she had her baby.
She loved it and wanted to keep it. As soon as she was
able to leave the home she got a room in a cheap rooming house and started out to look for work, leaving the
baby in a home until she should be able to support it.
She did not know how to work and had no experience or
recommendations and could not get steady employment.
She walked the streets until her shoes were worn out,
went hungry in order to have money for room rent, but
her landlady finally put her out. When that happened,
a girl who lived in the same house took her in.

About that time a moral wave struck Portland and the
sporting houses in the north end were being closed. The
women from those houses were scattered all over town.
Every hotel and rooming house held its quota of girls,

and some went into residential districts. It was one of those women who took the girl in and made a prostitute of her. While in Portland on business I happened to meet the girl on the street. She was delighted to see me but became embarrassed and ashamed when I found out what she was doing. She was terribly homesick to see her mother and sisters, but very bitter toward her father. She wanted to get out of the life she was in but did not know how. I took her to the office of my doctor friend, who had helped her get into the home for girls, and he readily consented to find her a decent place to live until she could get permanent employment. A few months later he wrote that she had committed suicide.

I often think of her—she was the first girl to come to me "in trouble"—and I always remember what a lovely girl she was when I first knew her. There have been many since.

Some of the girls who sought my aid were lucky enough to have decent parents who stood by them. Many later became wives and mothers.

Some were relieved of their pregnancy through the aid of women friends, or went off somewhere to secure an abortion and came back without anyone being the wiser. But when the pious and saintly old sisters of the reform group did find out, the girls were maligned and gossiped about until they were obliged to leave town.

A few of the girls were lucky enough to achieve a sudden and unexpected marriage. Then the virtuous old sisters of the community recorded the date of the wedding and computed the time elapsed before the baby arrived. In such cases I would announce a seven or eight months' baby.

Now my statement as to the length of the period of gestation in a case of this kind held weight with the virtuous old sisters in direct proportion to the popularity of the mother within the folds of the redeemed. If she happened to be one who attended church regularly, the weight of opinion would confirm my solemn statement that an eight months' baby had been born. But if she belonged to the other element, nothing I could say had any weight whatever, and I was considered either a liar or a plain fool.

A large percentage of public women are girls from small towns of the strictest morals, towns that would not tolerate a sporting house.

I am not attempting here to advance any argument in favor of prostitution or to advocate indiscriminate abortion, as I am not in favor of either, and if I were, this book is not the proper place for a discussion of the subjects. I am simply attempting to relate some of my experiences in practice. Furthermore, I have no plan or theory for the control or eradication of the evils.

Most such critics were subnormal or poorly sexed persons who believed the Creator made a serious mistake when he created man with sexual passion. They had repressed and distorted their own passion until they had developed repression complexes which made them hostile and hateful toward those who were normal, and they sought to correct the big mistake the Creator had made by destroying all passion in others or preventing it from functioning. Some of them thought the best way to stop the evil would be to persecute and prosecute the unfortunate girls and either put them in jail or run them out of town, shifting the responsibility onto other communities.

It has been my experience that it is the people who know the least about those things and are the least qualified to deal with either problem who want to regulate them according to their own ideas and prejudices. They were always the ones who made the most noise and commotion about prostitution, in that town at any rate.

CHAPTER 10

The Worst Enemy Is Ignorance

LATE one cold winter afternoon, I arrived back in town from a call fifty miles to the north to find a call had been waiting most of the day for me to see a boy who was suffering severely with inflammatory rheumatism on a homestead forty-five miles south of town.

I made a few hurried visits in town and was off without stopping to eat. For the last thirty miles of the trip the snow was between two and three feet deep; the night was bitter cold, the road scarcely broken. I did not get to the homestead until near daybreak.

I found a boy of seventeen very sick, wailing and moaning with severe pain in his badly swollen joints. His father and two neighbors were doing what was termed "settin' up" with him, while the others of the large family and numerous neighbors were sleeping in all parts of the big log cabin and in various parts of the barn. After I had worked with him for an hour, he was sufficiently relieved to fall asleep—the first restful sleep he had had in two days.

I then asked the boy's father if I might have something to eat. I had been driving in the bitter cold for twenty-four hours without food. The homesteader hesitated a moment and then started for the kitchen, a lean-to affair of logs built onto the north end of the cabin, and I

HYMN TO THOSE IN THE ARMED FORCES

Eternal Father, strong to save,
Whose arm doth bind the restless wave,
Who bidd'st the mighty ocean deep,
Its own appointed limits keep;
O hear us when we cry to Thee
For those in peril on the sea.

Creator Who dost from above
Observe Thy sons with eyes of love,
Who canst preserve where'er they be
Our men who fight for house and Thee;
O put Thou forth a guiding hand,
For those in peril on the land.

Almighty, who canst from on high,
Protect our flyers in the sky
And guide each pilot in his plane
The length and breadth of Thy domain:
O hearken to our fervent prayer,
For those in peril in the air.

O Trinity of love and power,
Our forces shield in danger's hour;
From peril, onslaught, fire and foe
Protect them where-so-e'er they go;
Thus ever may there rise to Thee
Glad hymns from air and land and sea.

Captain Richard W. Bates, U.S.N.
in collaboration with the
Reverend Laurision L. Scaife, S.T.D.

thoughtlessly followed him. The sight that greeted me at the threshold caused serious doubts to arise in my mind.

In the center of the kitchen was a table of rough planks large enough to seat sixteen or eighteen people. The table was strewn with a disorderly array of dirty dishes and the remains of the last meal. A large platter in the center of the table held one little strip of badly burned bacon, timidly thrusting one curled-up corner above a sea of congealed grease. At one end was a platter with two little cold biscuits on it, and at the other end a bowl with a tablespoonful of cold soggy beans. A black, smoky coffee pot of about a gallon capacity, apparently empty, stood on the big wood range near the wall.

With evident embarrassment my host eyed the scene a moment, muttering to himself, and then started on a determined search of the kitchen. The search yielded little of promise as far as breakfast was concerned.

"Doc, she sure looks like the grub is kind'a low fur tha time bein'," he said. "There's been so much company since Alf got bad they've jest about cleaned us out 'a grub. We generally have enough jerky an' canned venison to last through 'til the deer drift back in tha spring, but tha deep snow come earlier than I figgered las' fall an' tha mowich all migrated down onto tha desert before we got our usual supply. Tha river an' lakes froze over before we got tha trout barrels full, an' we jest et tha last of the smoked trout the other day. There ain't much on hand but some rice an' beans an' canned huckleberries an' sech as that, but I'll go to tha store an' lay in a supply of grub—I was figgerin' on goin' to tha store to-day anyhow."

Fortunately, there was a general store and post-office

only ten miles away, and the homesteader was soon on the way in his home-made sled.

As soon as he was out of sight I went to the kitchen and ate the two little biscuits, the cold beans, and the little strip of bacon, but that only whetted my hunger.

Tired and irritable, I went back into the big living room and sat down in a home-made rocking chair in front of the big fireplace to doze.

The lob cabin was a huge affair with ample space for the large family, with a lean-to log kitchen at one end and two lean-to bedrooms of logs at the other end. A ladder of lodge-pole pine led up to a big loft, or attic, over the living room, where a part of the large family had sleeping quarters.

It was soon daylight and the housewife and two daughters came down the ladder and went to the kitchen to light a fire and make a bluff at getting breakfast. Visiting neighbors soon began to appear from various parts of the house and barn and gathered around the fireplace in the living room as that was the only warm place in the house.

Soon fifteen people gathered in the living room where the sick boy was sleeping and made so much noise laughing and talking that it woke him up. I was annoyed.

"Will you all please step outside a moment?" I said to the assemblage, "I have something I want to tell you."

They looked surprised but slowly filed out of the door and stood in the snow outside. My little speech was very much to the point, and ran something like this:

"Alfred is very sick. The rheumatism has seriously affected his heart. Any noise or excitement will make him worse. The commotion you made by gathering in the living room just now woke him from the first restful sleep he has had in two days. I know, of course, that you all came here to help Alfred and want to do anything you can to help him.

"The one thing you can do is to go home and stay there." And then I'm afraid I waxed a little bit caustic. "You have heard all the news, discussed all the scandal and gossip since ten years back; you've eaten all the grub in the house and your chances for breakfast are mighty slim. The sooner you go home the better for everybody concerned, including yourselves."

I don't remember all I said, but from the expressions on their faces I judged it was more than enough. Some were embarrassed; some were offended; I didn't give a hoot. I left them there in the snow and returned to my sick boy.

The visitors, one by one, came back to the house to pack up and leave while I went into one of the vacated rooms and crawled in between the blankets with most of my clothes on, and slept until called for breakfast.

The homesteader and his wife could not understand why the visitors left so suddenly until I explained briefly. The wife was shocked and much disturbed; but the father was tickled to death.

The news of my breaking up the party in such a discourteous manner spread like wild fire and was the beginning of a complete change in the custom of neighbors visiting the sick in droves for a protracted celebration.

Customs of visiting the sick in town were different, but just as pernicious. One of the worst offenders was a minister who was determined to save the souls of all of the sick.

He was a small man with a long gray beard, a greatly

inflated personality and a prodigious appetite. With his double-breasted frock coat, which was a foot too long, his over-long trousers piled in wrinkles about his ankles, and his faded, odd-shaped high-crowned derby, he looked like a character in a cartoon. He had an uncontrollable mania for calling on every sick person and was extremely persistent in his efforts to save the patient's soul before he should die and go to Hell.

He timed his visits to the sick so he would be in the house at meal time and was never known to refuse an invitation to dine. Once fortified with a superabundance of victuals, he went after the sick person's soul in a most persistent manner and sometimes, by sheer endurance, overcame the wiles of the devil and the resistance of the sufferer.

When admitted to the sick room of a patient of mine, who was very ill with a heart disease, he said abruptly to him, "One of your friends has just told me that the doctor says your case is serious. Are you prepared to die and meet your Maker?"

It was a great effort for the sick man to talk, but the preacher plied him with endless questions demanding answers until he became so exhausted from talking, his wife had to ask the preacher to leave.

I was called and found the patient near collapse. I was mad clear through. I went after the preacher rough-shod the following day and told him his visit had done the patient considerable harm. He seemed surprised and did not like it when I asked him not to call on any more of my patients without my permission.

He told me it was his sacred duty to save the souls of all the sick if possible. He firmly believed he should round up all the maverick sinners and drive them by force, if necessary, into the fold of the redeemed. If the maverick fought the rope and was scarred up while he was putting the Lord's brand on him, it did not matter so long as his soul was saved. But after some discussion with the minister, I gained the impression he would respect my wishes thereafter and not call on my patients without permission, but I was mistaken.

A few days later I went to see a very nervous woman who was in no condition to see visitors and noticed the minister's faded derby in the hall when I entered. As I looked into the sick room I saw the preacher kneeling at the bedside and heard him fervently imploring the Lord to save the dear sister's soul. His back was toward the door and he did not see me enter the room just as he pronounced the last solemn and impressive "Ah-h-h-h-men."

Without a word I seized him by the coat collar and the ample seat of his over-long trousers and hustled him out of the house. I threw the faded derby out after him and shut the door. When I returned to the sick room the patient was enjoying a hearty laugh. That visit may have accomplished a little good, as it was the first time the patient had laughed during her illness, but that was the last time the preacher called on a patient of mine without permission.

There was another member of the clergy who did not use any judgment about calling on the sick. He did not call on them as often as the aforementioned preacher, but what he lacked in frequency he made up for in staying qualities.

One day he called on a woman patient of mine who had

a very active and troublesome dysentery, with three or four bowel movements an hour. He planted himself in the comfortable chair in her bedroom and stayed most of the afternoon. The poor distressed woman was too timid to get up and go to the bathroom, clad only in her scant nighty, in the presence of her distinguished gentleman visitor, so she had to lie there soiling the bed all that long, glorious afternoon. I apprised the reverend gentleman of the plight of the unfortunate woman the next day and suggested he ask me about the advisability of calling on sick persons in the future, stressing the admonition that a sick call should never be longer than twenty minutes.

But I never fully succeeded in educating people to make their visits to the sick short. It was also difficult to make them understand that a sick person should sleep during the night, and not have someone "settin' up with him" to entertain him.

One Saturday noon an old doctor who had recently located in a little town fifty miles away called me in consultation on a case that was thought to be spinal meningitis.

A strong, healthy boy of six had been playing with his toys on the floor in a room where his mother sat sewing on the previous Thursday afternoon. He suddenly stopped playing, turned pale, vomited, and in a few minutes had a convulsion. He continued to vomit and have convulsions and his parents finally called the local doctor Friday night. There were several cases of spinal meningitis scattered over the state at that time and because of the convulsions the boy's mother was sure he was coming down with spinal meningitis. The local doctor did not agree with her and insisted on calling me for consultation.

I arrived at the boy's home in company with the local doctor about six in the evening and found he was still having convulsions and vomiting fecal matter from the intestines, indicating intestinal obstruction. Examination disclosed a large, hard, tumor-like mass in the abdomen, which caused the abdominal wall to bulge noticeably. The principal diagnostic symptoms of meningitis were missing and I made a diagnosis of intussusception (telescoping of the bowel), to which the local doctor agreed.

I explained the case to the worried parents and told them that an operation to relieve the intestinal obstruction offered the only chance for recovery. Already greatly worried, they became almost frantic at the thought of an operation. The father stated belligerently that he was opposed to surgery under any circumstances, that he had never known an operation to be successful, and accused doctors who had operated on an uncle of murder.

"I know damn well he didn't need no operation in the first place, an' he wouldn't 'a died if the damn doctors hadn't 'a cut him all to pieces," he said heatedly.

While I argued with the parents about an operation, we began preparing for it, but the argument grew so heated I told them that if they would not consent to it I would go home as there was nothing else to do.

When I began to pick up my things to leave, the mother became frantic and gave her consent. I then waited for a time while she tried to persuade the father; but when I saw she was accomplishing nothing I again picked up my bags and started to go. Then the father suddenly changed his attitude.

"Will you guarantee the boy will live and git well if you operate?" he asked.

"No I will not," I answered. "He has about one chance in fifty to get well with the operation, but absolutely none without it."

"Well, if he's got to die I want him to die whole an' not all cut up to pieces," he retorted.

"All right, if that's the way you feel about it I'll go home," I said, as I once again picked up my bags.

"Well, all right, all right then, go ahead and operate if you're so damned anxious to cut him up, but I'll tell you one thing right now. If what you say is wrong with him ain't what's the matter with him, or he dies from the operation, you ain't goin' ta git out'a this town alive—do you understand that?"

That made me boiling mad. If I had been a little older, wiser, and more experienced, I would have withdrawn from the case right there, but I was young and green and so filled with the high ideals of the profession that I thought I must save the boy's life if possible.

The local doctor sent for a woman who had worked under him as a practical nurse and preparations were soon finished. The kitchen table was prepared for an operating table and the boy placed upon it. The atmosphere and surroundings were tense and charged with enmity and unfriendly feeling. The arguments and friction had set my nerves on edge, and the father's threat had made me mad and determined. Conditions were certainly not favorable for a green country doctor to be undertaking an operation like that one. It was an operation I had practiced on the cadaver but never attempted on a living patient. When the time came to begin the operation, I would have given a good deal if I could have backed out, but that would have robbed the boy of his only chance for recovery.

With all the determination I could muster I began the operation. The responsibility and nervous strain I was under made my hands tremble in spite of my best efforts to control them. The father had demanded that he be shown the strangulated bowel before he gave his full consent for the operation. For that reason he was allowed to stay in the room, but at a safe distance from the table. His presence annoyed me and I did not want him to see my hands trembling.

When the abdomen was opened, the mass of strangulated bowel popped right up into the incision, and the father was allowed to have a good look at it. He was then told to get out of the room and stay out until he was sent for. If anything went wrong during the operation I did not want him to rush into the room until I was prepared for him.

The terrific strain and responsibility made the sweat run out of me as though I was in a steam bath. It was fortunate that the practical nurse was there to mop my brow and keep the sweat out of my eyes. One section of the intestine about six inches long was gangrenous and had to be resected (removed), and the cut ends united again. That was a more difficult procedure on the small boy than on the full grown cadaver. Somehow we managed to get through with the operation with the boy still alive, but severely shocked.

We set feverishly to work to resuscitate him. For what seemed a long time there was no perceptible change, but at last his pulse became stronger and his respiration deeper. I happened to glance up at the window and saw it was daylight. The last moment in which I had been conscious of the time it was midnight.

When we thought his condition good enough to leave him with the nurse, the old doctor took me to his house for breakfast. After breakfast we went back to the boy and found him still rallying.

The local doctor insisted that I stay on the case until the boy was out of danger. The practical nurse was given the principal nursing responsibility for the case, but could devote only a part of her time to it because of her work at home. I left detailed instructions for the boy's care in writing. By the time I was ready to start home, the father was in a more pleasant mood. He asked me when the boy could have "something to eat" and when I told him it would be a week or so before he could have solid food of any kind he at once became belligerent again, and another argument followed.

"That kid ain't had nothin' to eat since Thursday noon an' he's got to git some grub into him to give him some strength if you expect him to git well from this here operation," he declared.

I explained why the boy should have only liquids for several days, but the father remained sullen and seemed unconvinced.

As I dozed in the buggy on the way home, I continually dreamed that a serious complication developed and the boy died. The local doctor telephoned the following day that the boy was doing as well as could be expected. The next day I went to see him and found his condition fairly satisfactory. He had severe gas pains for two days but on the fourth day he said he was hungry and asked for fried potatoes when he smelled them cooking. That led to an argument. The father finally conceded that fried potatoes might be a little heavy, but he thought some nice mashed potato would be good for him.

I planned to see the boy on the fifth post-operative day, but just before daylight I had an urgent call to a ranch thirty-five miles from town in another direction. On the return trip I found a ranch hand waiting in the road to intercept me. The operator at central office had an urgent call for me. I knew something had happened to the boy and rushed to the telephone while the buckaroo held my team. Central told me the boy's father wanted me to hurry down there—"the boy was very bad."

I exchanged my team for the best one on the ranch and lit out for the boy's home. Instead of going back to town I cut across the desert through the sage brush to the road I wanted to take and saved several miles. I then pushed the team to the limit for about fifty miles, but when I arrived at the boy's house he was dead. The mother was hysterical with grief, the father sullen and defiant. The nurse was considerably upset for fear she was to blame.

She told me the boy was fairly comfortable the day before, talked about things he wanted to eat. The family had fried chicken for supper that evening and the boy had asked for some when he smelled it cooking in the kitchen, but she refused him. She left him just before supper was ready and went home to get supper for her own family. Shortly after midnight the boy's father came after her saying, "I wish you'd come over; the kid's crying with the belly ache."

She found the boy crying with a greatly distended abdomen. The local doctor was sent for, but he was far away in the country on a confinement case where there was no telephone. The nurse did all she could for the boy, then sent a call for me as soon as the telephone office was open in the morning, but I had already gone to the country.

I accused the father of giving the boy fried chicken but he stoutly denied it. The local doctor and I asked for a post-mortem, but the father sullenly refused, and stubbornly insisted that the operation had killed the boy, just as he had expected it would.

When he began to get nasty I told him very bluntly that if he would not give us written consent for an autopsy I would swear to a complaint charging him with involuntary manslaughter and demand an autopsy by the county coroner, who was a physician in the county seat. He then grudgingly gave his consent.

When the boy's stomach was opened it was found to contain a large quantity of fried chicken, mashed potato, canned peas, bread, and gravy, which had partially digested and then fermented into a foul, sour-smelling mess. The gases formed by the fermentation had distended the stomach until it was greatly dilated and pressed on the diaphragm and solar plexus, stopping the action of the heart.

When the old doctor saw the dilated stomach filled with the mess of fermented food his eyes filled with tears and he left the room. I was too mad to shed tears and confronted the father with the evidence.

He sullenly admitted giving the boy some of the food but insisted that he had not given him all that was found in the stomach. He would not believe that the food was the cause of the boy's death. I told him bluntly that he was a damn fool, an ignoramus, and a few other things that would not look well in print; but even giving full expression to my feelings gave me little satisfaction or consolation. The boy was dead and surgery was blamed for it.

As far as I know that was the first intestinal resection ever attempted in the county.

Aside from the boy's death, the keenest disappointment to me was the realization that the boy's parents had so little faith in my integrity and intentions. Although I gave them every assurance that an operation offered the only possible chance to save the boy's life, they still seemed to think that I wanted to operate simply because I was fond of doing surgery. If they could only have known how I dreaded and feared that operation and how quickly I would have turned the case over to a better surgeon had there been one available, they would have been surprised.

Having been reared in a doctor's family, I had always been impressed with the keen sense of responsibility and the humanitarianism basically inherent in all doctors of the regular medical profession. I had taken it for granted that everyone recognized those qualities in all doctors. I expected the boy's parents would not only trust me when I was doing my best to save his life but would also show a little appreciation.

Their attitude was of course due to ignorance. I seemed to be finding my way blocked or beset with difficulties on every hand because of ignorance.

CHAPTER 11

Horse Thieves and Cattle Rustlers

IN FEBRUARY, after a week of intermittent snowing, there was about a foot and a half of snow all over the lower country. But when the temperature rose, heavy rains fell until the streams were higher than they had ever been in the memory of the oldest settlers.

Late one Sunday evening a strange horseman came splashing across the range through the slush to the house of a rancher who lived at the end of a local telephone line. Without dismounting he shouted to the rancher to telephone for a doctor to go out to an old, deserted homestead, about eighty-five miles from town as the crow flies, to attend a man hurt in an accident.

"Have the doctor get out there as soon as he can," were the horseman's parting words, as he wheeled his horse and rode away.

The deserted homestead was near the foot of a butte formed of lava and cinders, five or six hundred feet high, standing near the edge of a vast sweep of level plain. Its top and slopes were covered with a growth of jack pine and juniper trees, with a cluster of trees at the top which gave it the appearance of having a sharp black point when seen from a distance. At some time in the past a stranger came into the country and took a homestead near the foot of the butte, which was in a section of the country used for cattle range. He built a log cabin, a log barn, and some corrals with logs cut from the butte, and dug a well which still held water most of the year. He had apparently intended to go into the sheep business.

The buildings were still in a fair state of preservation, but the homesteader had mysteriously disappeared, without its being known exactly when or how. It was rumored he had gone the way of so many of those who attempt to run sheep in a cattle country.

Since his disappearance the cabin had been uninhabited, except when used for headquarters at the time of the yearly roundups for that section of the range, and it appeared strange that anyone should be there at this time of year. I always answered all calls that came, however, and was soon on the road.

The only road running through that section passed to the east of the butte and crossed a stream where there was no bridge. I planned to take a team and buggy to a cattle ranch forty-five miles on the way, and go horseback from there to the butte.

Traveling over the slushy road was a little slow and I did not reach the cattle ranch until daylight, just as the cow hands were filing into the cook shack for breakfast. The foreman called a couple of cow hands to take my team and put it up and saddle one of his best horses for me while he led me in to breakfast. While we ate hastily, I told the foreman all about the strange call to the butte. He was as mystified about it as I was.

"Some of that goddam bunch of high desert hoss thieves has run into some bad luck," the foreman ventured. "I'd like to ride over there with you and pot a couple of the damn wallopers."

But the foreman could not go as the flood was washing out a part of his irrigation system and the cow hands did not work well with shovels unless they had a boss to keep them at it. It is beneath the dignity of a first-class cowboy to work with a shovel.

After breakfast the foreman helped me tie a pair of large saddle bags, which I had brought along to hold my equipment, onto the saddle, and I started for the butte.

The rain had ceased and the sun was just pushing his fiery rim above the horizon into great bands of gorgeous coloring for a glorious sunrise as I reached the edge of the plain. Far to the east the Blue Mountains etched their jagged contour. A hundred miles to the west the Cascade Mountains stood out in bold relief, forming a mammoth serrated wall on the west. Forty miles to the south the butte toward which I was riding stood out clearly, looking like a little mound the size of a haystack with its sharp black point clearly outlined against the bright blue sky.

Great masses of dark clouds hung around the Cascade Peaks at the southern end of the range and extended far down the slopes toward the plain. There was no road or trail for me to follow but I did not need anything to guide me as long as I could see the butte—all I had to do was to ride straight to it. I had a good horse and put mile after mile behind as I hurried along through the soft slush all morning. The big bank of clouds in the southwest came down the mountain slopes and out over the plain toward me at a much more rapid rate than I seemed to be approaching the butte.

Shortly after noon I came to an old river channel that was usually dry but now, because of the unprecedented rain and melting snow, was bank-full of yellow muddy water. I rode along the bank until I came to a suitable place to cross where the banks were not too steep. I dismounted, untied the saddle bags and threw them over my shoulders, then led the horse down to the edge and waited while he drank. I remounted to go across, but the wise old bronc did not want to go into the cold water and stopped at the edge with a loud snort. A dig with the spurs sent him splashing into the water that grew deeper and deeper until the horse was swimming strongly by the time we reached the middle of the swift current.

I was soaking wet almost to the shoulders when we were across but managed to hold the saddle bags with my equipment out of the water. The cold bath put new life into the horse, but I was chilled through and shook with chattering teeth in the cold breeze that was by that time blowing out of the west. I dismounted, tied the saddle bags on, and ran along leading the horse until I was completely out of breath trying to get warm.

I wanted to build a fire and dry my clothes, but my matches were wet, and it would have been next to impossible to start a fire with the wet sage brush. I also realized that the storm clouds would soon obscure the butte and I would have nothing to guide me, as I had no compass.

The now steady breeze was pushing the storm clouds rapidly nearer and the temperature was dropping. I remounted and spurred the horse into a gallop. Before I realized it the storm was upon me and the temperature dropped sharply. The first little snowflakes danced about me in the wind like tiny blowing feathers.

I fully realized the danger of the situation. In a few

minutes the butte would be blotted from my sight and I would be way out in the wide desert with nothing to guide me. I was tired, wet, cold and hungry, my clothes soaking, and night was fast approaching.

I stopped the horse to think, without taking my eyes from the butte, and sat there shivering, trying to decide what to do. If I went on and missed the butte I would wander over the desert in my wet clothes and freeze before morning. If I turned back to the ranch I would have my tracks to follow until the snow covered them; then if I gave the horse his head he would take me back to the ranch. I thought of the patients back in town who would be needing me before I could get back to them if I went on.

I thought of the injured man at the butte who was expecting me. He might be a horse thief for all I knew, but his life might be lost, and I would be criminally negligent if I did not go on. I had never turned back before, no matter how tough the going.

As I sat there shivering in the cold wind I determined to go on and try to make the butte, although I well knew it was a hazardous thing to attempt.

I watched the little black point of the butte gradually fade from sight in the falling snow, and as it was obliterated I picked out a large clump of sage brush directly in line with me and the point of the butte and rode toward it. Before I got up to it I picked out a second clump and rode past and on toward the second. Just before I reached the second clump, I picked out a third. Thus I rode all that long, cold, miserable, wretched afternoon, keeping my eyes constantly on the line of direction I was following, without glancing to either side for an instant. The wind, I knew, was blowing directly from the west and I kept it on my right cheek, and that helped me to keep my bearings.

I suffered more and more as the temperature fell. My wet clothes were soon frozen stiff. I was afraid my feet were frozen, as there was no feeling in them. After suffering severely from the cold for a long time, I began to feel the cold less and thought the temperature must be rising. I was very tired and sleepy. I had an almost uncontrollable desire to stop the horse and doze in the saddle for just a few moments, but did not dare to take my eyes from the line of direction I was following.

After a while it took all my will power and determination to rouse myself and keep awake. Finally the realization began to penetrate my benumbed consciousness that I was beginning to experience the first unmistakable symptoms of freezing. I was too tired and miserable to care much. Freezing to death did not seem so terrible after all. As my will power and determination began to flag, the snowstorm seemed to take on the personality of some evil genie that mocked and laughed at my receding courage.

I roused myself with all my will in an effort to appraise my situation and think in a logical and cool-headed manner. My head was cold enough, but not so logical! The day was almost gone and night was rapidly coming on. My first thought was that I was lost. I estimated that I had traveled more than forty miles since daylight, although the footing was poor for the horse and traveling slow. I thought I had come more than far enough to be at the butte and had passed it without seeing it in the falling snow.

I roused myself for a final desperate effort and pushed on toward the next clump of sage. The horse began to annoy me by wanting to turn off to the right and head more into the wind. I pulled him back to the course a time or two, but he went only a few steps before trying to turn off into the wind again.

I was still rational enough to realize that was not the natural thing for him to do. Stock on the range always drift with the storm, with their tails to the wind. The horse had been pulling off to the right for several minutes before I had the good sense to look in that direction. For a moment I saw nothing, but as I sat there gazing off through the flickering curtain of falling snowflakes, a long dark shadow loomed faintly in the distance. I started the horse toward it and he pricked up his ears, whinnied, and quickened his pace. The shadow began to assume the form of a corral, but that did not mean anything until I began to realize that the only corrals in that part of the country were at the old homestead by the butte.

My head whirled and I reeled in the saddle as I saw flashes of light and bright spots before my eyes. I stopped the horse to get control of myself. As we started on, the horse threw up his head and whinnied again, and then I heard a shout, far away through the falling snow. I gave the horse his head; then everything went black before my eyes. The whole world seemed to be a great void of total blackness, with here and there little sparks of glittering fire and great streaks of blinding light shooting through it like flashes of jagged lightning.

I never clearly remembered what happened for a time after that, but when I was again fully conscious of myself and surroundings, I was in the cabin at the butte and it was night. My frozen clothing was off and I was on the floor, wrapped in a blanket, before a little sheet-iron camp stove that was red hot in spots. How good that heat did feel!

The cabin was lighted by a lantern hung from a rafter and there were four men in it. One was mumbling and stirring restlessly in a bunk built into the wall. Two others sat on a bed of small pine boughs with blankets spread over them on the floor, their backs to the wall. A tall, rather wild-looking fellow with bushy red whiskers and long sandy hair seemed to be the master of ceremonies. He wore a red flannel shirt, high-heeled boots of expensive make with fancy patterns stitched on them, and a wide sombrero on the back of his head. From descriptions I had heard I took him to be Grizzly Colton. He was an often discussed character among the stockmen and was suspected of being the leader of a band of horse thieves and cattle rustlers that infested the high desert. He had no ranch and seldom worked on any, although he was a top cow hand and bronco buster, but he owned a small brand of horses that ran on the open range. Although his brand of horses was his only known source of income, he always seemed to have money and was known to have an account in a bank.

The men on the bed and on the floor eyed me in silence, but Grizzly made up for their lack of conversation with a continuous string of talk.

"By God, Doc, I'm shore glad you're here," he said. "Tex's been plumb out of his head most of tha time since night 'a fore last. You shore made mighty damn good time—it wouldn't sprised me none if ya hadn't a got here before tomorry. I figgered more'n likely you'd be ta hell an' gone on a call somewheres las' night an' wouldn't git started 'fore this mornin'.''

"Lucky figgered you'd be comin' with a team by tha road an' acrost tha big flat, but hell-up-a-mountain! I knowed there couldn't nobody git acrost Bear Crick in no rig in all this here goddam flood. When that snow come up this afternoon I figgered you'd shore as hell be hittin' fer them heavy junipers on yon side of tha slope where ya cud build ya a hell-roarin' fire an' hole up 'til she broke an' you'd have tha stars ta tell ya where in the hell ya was at. You was shore plumb tuckered out when I pulled ya of'fen yer hoss."

Grizzly offered me food but I was too tired and miserable to eat. Every bone in my body ached and I was still dizzy and light-headed. Then he handed me a tin cup of black coffee.

"Here, git a little chickory into yer gizzard—it'll do ya good besides helpin' ya," he said.

The man in the bunk, called Tex, stirred and cursed loudly, and Grizzly went over to him while I sipped coffee.

"What happened to Tex?" I asked when Grizzly returned.

"He's been shot up some, Doc, kinda bad I reckon."

"How did it happen?" I persisted.

"Well," said Grizzly, hesitantly, as he looked at me with a cold glitter in his narrowed eyes, "he must'a been in front of the bygod gun when tha damn thing went off, I reckon. But that part of it ain't none of yer goddam business, Doc. I got ya out here ta fix tha boys up pronto so's we kin git ta hell out'a here, an' that's all in Chrise world ya got ta worry 'bout, 'ceptin' ta keep yer goddam mouth shet plumb tight from right now on. If ya keep yer goddam mouth shet 'bout it ya'll git yer pay fer it some day, but if ya ever let a yap out'a yer face ya won't never need no bygod money. Savvy?"

I understood his lingo perfectly and had no doubt of his sincerity.

My clothes were still wet. Wrapped in a blanket, I examined Tex, while Grizzly held the lantern. I gave him a hypodermic of hyoscine, morphine, and cactine. Then I examined the other two men. Each one had a flesh wound that looked like the work of a soft-nosed rifle bullet, but the wounds were not infected or of a serious nature. They had been shot ten days before. I put my clothes on before they were completely dry and ate a meal of camp bread, beans, jerked meat, stewed apricots, and coffee, which Grizzly had prepared. By that time Tex had the full effect of the hypo and I dressed his wounds. A soft-nosed rifle bullet had shattered an inch and a half of the bone of his left arm, half way between the elbow and shoulder. A second bullet had struck his right leg just above the knee, penetrated to the deep fascia, ranged upward and come out in the groin. It had carried a wad of hair from his bright yellow angora chaps half way up the leg and left it there. Pus was discharging from both ends of the wound. This was the wound that was causing the fever and delirium. Since the arm did not appear to be infected it was dressed first.

The little splinters of bone and strips of necrotic flesh were trimmed away, a drain inserted, the muscles stitched, and the arm was put in splints made from the pine shakes taken from the roof of the barn.

In the poor light of the lantern Grizzly held for me, I

made a long incision at each end of the leg wound, removed the wad of hair, and swabbed the whole infected sinus with a solution of carbolic acid and alcohol. Tex swore eloquently but did not flinch. Drains were inserted and the long incisions were partially closed with stitches.

As soon as the dressings were finished, I rolled in a blanket across one end of the bed of pine boughs and was soon wrapped in the deep sleep of exhaustion.

It seemed I had been asleep only a few minutes when Grizzly woke me at daylight. We took Tex from his bunk and laid him on the floor where the light was the best, where I did a complete dressing of his wounds, then showed Grizzly how to do it. Tex was rational and his temperature had dropped—I was amazed at the improvement he had made.

The wounds of the other two rustlers were pretty well healed.

After breakfast I began packing up my equipment to leave but Grizzly objected. He wanted me to stay at least another day, as he realized Tex was not entirely out of danger. After a long discussion I finally won the argument by telling him that if I did not get back to the cattle ranch that night, the people there would think I had gotten lost in the snowstorm and would come to look for me, would find him and his pals. He did not want to be found just then and consented to my going.

While he went to the barn for my horse, I took bits of charred wood from the stove and blackened my face, eyelids and forehead, to break the glare of the bright sunshine on the new snow that I would have to ride through all day. Grizzly helped tie my saddle bags onto the saddle, cautioned me very pointedly not to tell anyone about what I had seen, and with the sun several hours high I started home, intending to ride hard and make the cattle ranch by dark.

The new snow covered the whole world in a blanket of dazzling white as far as the eye could reach in every direction; the sun was shining brightly, but the day was cold and crisp. Except for some frozen-over pools, the old river bed that had swum my horse the day before was empty and I crossed without danger of getting wet.

It was after dark when I rode into the cattle ranch and gave a loud "hello" that brought the foreman out of his shack. Most of the ranch people had gone to bed, but some of the boys were playing cards in the cook house. The foreman roused the cook to get me something to eat and sent two of the boys to hitch up my team. While I ate, he plied me with questions about the trip, but I had a story all thought out for him.

I told the foreman that I arrived at the cabin at dark the night before and found it empty, although signs showed people had been there that day. I could not tell how many had been there or which way they went when they left, as the new snow had covered all tracks.

"The man so seriously hurt must have died, and the others wanting to bury him in a real graveyard had taken the body away before I arrived," was the only explanation I could offer.

The foreman seemed to believe my story but was greatly mystified by the whole affair. He suspected that some of the rustlers had been in a shooting scrape. After discussing the matter, he agreed with me that the best thing we could do would be to keep quiet and see what we could find out about the affair. I drove home in the

cold, crisp night under the big, brilliant, glowing desert
stars, half expecting to be called to see Tex again, for
I was not sure all the infection in his leg had been
checked.

One hot, dry day the following summer, I walked down
to the bank building after lunch and sat down on the
edge of the board sidewalk in the shade to finish my
cigar before going upstairs to the office. Thinking of the
cold trip to the butte the previous winter, and wonder-
ing if I should tell the sheriff about it, I looked off down
the road that was a continuation of the street and saw a
dust-covered horseman approaching. He looked vaguely
familiar and I noticed he was eyeing me closely.

He reined the horse in toward the sidewalk and I saw
it was Lucky, whom I had seen at the butte.

"Howdy, Doc, I got somethin' fer ya," he said, as he
gave me a beckoning nod to come out to him.

"Here 's yer money fer tha trip out to tha butte las'
winter," he announced as he handed me a little buckskin
bag. He touched his horse with the spurs and rode on up
the street into town while I stood gaping at him, too surprised even to thank him for the money.

I took the bag up to the office and found it contained
the exact amount I had told Grizzly I would charge for
the trip, all in five, ten, and twenty dollar gold pieces.

I was curious to know what became of Tex and hoped
Lucky would come to the office, but he did not show up.
He stayed in town on a spree a few days but I had no
chance to talk to him.

I ran into Grizzly and Lucky a few times—sometimes
under suspicious circumstances—during the months that
followed, but did not talk to either of them. Late in the

following winter I met Grizzly quite unexpectedly.

Arrived back in town one cold night after a long trip, I met a group of young business men when I stepped into the post office for my mail, and one of the group proposed we all go to the log cabin for a drink to dispel the cold. The log cabin was the "highest class" saloon in town and a favorite gathering place for the more convivial of the prominent citizens.

We had just lined up at the bar when the street door opened and a buckaroo wearing a sombrero, a mackinaw of bright colors, overalls, boots, and a fair-sized jag, walked in. He sat down in a rawhide bottomed chair by the big wood stove near the center of the room with his elbows on his knees and his chin in his hands. He soon went to sleep and tumbled from the chair to the floor. The bartender helped him up and gave him a shake to rouse him. We all looked around and I saw it was Grizzly. He had had a hair cut and a shave which changed his appearance so much I did not recognize him when he first came in. He was a keen-looking fellow when barbered up with his fine physique and clean-cut features. He saw me looking at him and said, "Howdy, Doc."

"Hello, Grizzly, have a drink with us," I said.

One of my companions, Jimmy Sawhill, a recently arrived tenderfoot from Ohio with a quizzical smile, surprised that I should ask the drunken buckaroo to drink with us, said to Grizzly, as he nodded at me:

"Do you know this fellow?"

"Hell-up-a-mountain, I shore know Doc," said Grizzly, "I seen him one night when he was a damn sight colder 'n he is tonight."

"How did I get into the cabin that night?" I asked.

"There wasn't much to that, Doc, I jest pulled ya of'fen tha bronc an' kicked yer bygod tail into tha shack while ya was tryin' ta tell me ya was all in," he said.

Noting that Grizzly was in a good-natured talkative mood, I ordered another drink and asked more questions.

"What became of that fellow Tex?" I asked.

"Tex—Oh yes, him? That tough — — — — ya couldn't kill him," said Grizzly. "He got better an' lit out fer tha Pecos country down in Texas where he come from."

As our conversation continued the bartender and the boys with me became greatly interested and kept buying drinks to keep Grizzly talking. He talked about range wars, sheep shooting and cattle rustling; Jimmy Sawhill, who had heard about such things but did not know they still existed, was especially interested. When Jimmy changed the drinks to champagne for the bunch, Grizzly seemed actually to become more sober and talked more freely.

He did not give satisfactory answers to all my questions; he'd probably have incriminated himself if he had answered truthfully. But he did shed some light on several unsolved mysteries.

Time passed and the wine flowed freely, while the bartender and the boys with me listened with breathless interest. Finally I asked Grizzly who killed J. C. Conn, a stockman whose body had been found riddled with bullets a short time after five masked men had killed 2500 sheep belonging to Benham Brothers. Grizzly flared up.

"Goddam it, Doc, quit yer diggin' into me like that. If it hadn't a been fer me ya wouldn't a got back from the bygod butte that time you was out there."

"Why wouldn't I?"

"Cause the boys was goin' ta kill ya, that's why."

"Why didn't they do it?" I countered.

Grizzly hesitated a moment, as if at a loss for an answer, then with some irritation said, "Cause I was yer friend an' wouldn't stand fer it." Then he added hotly, as if it were an afterthought, "It might a been a goddam good thing if they had."

That last remark, with Grizzly's insulting tones, was too much for me, with all the mixed drinks I had taken. I took a swing at his jaw and the friendly little party became a lively rough-house. The bartender and my companions separated us and the party broke up.

I went off to bed to think over some of the things Grizzly had told me and to wonder if I should tell the sheriff. When I woke in the morning with a clear head, I decided it would be in better taste for me to let others do the telling; they had heard as much as I had.

Jimmy Sawhill came to the office that morning filled with suppressed excitement:

"Say, Doc, that was a mighty interesting and exciting evening we had last night. You ought to write a book about your experiences."

He was afraid Grizzly would nurse a grudge and proposed that some of the boys find him and make peace. He feared that Grizzly would waylay me some night when I was traveling alone over the desert. But I saw no more of Grizzly until the beginning of summer.

Then one morning early a buckaroo telephoned that Grizzly wanted me to come out to the Stanley-Davenport ranch east of town as soon as possible. I knew Grizzly was not working on that ranch and had no connection of any kind with it, but I had no suspicion of treachery. I rushed out there and found a young buckaroo about twenty lying unconscious in the bunk house.

Grizzly, with several buckaroos, had been rounding up wild horses on the range near one corner of the ranch. This boy, running his horse through a thick growth of juniper to head a band of horses others were chasing, suddenly saw a new wire fence loom up in front of him. He was going too fast to stop and tried to hurdle the fence but the horse's front feet hit the top wire and broke it. One end of the broken wire caught in the boy's spur, dragged him from the saddle of the falling horse and slapped him to the ground. He was picked up unconscious and carried to the bunk house on the ranch.

Grizzly was very fond of the boy and deeply concerned over the accident. He was grieved when I told him the boy's skull was fractured and he had no chance to recover, and sent immediately for an older brother who was riding on a ranch some distance away. Grizzly implored me to stay right with the boy and keep him alive if possible until the brother arrived, and I did. He was too deeply grieved to bear animosity toward anyone and the little incident in the log-cabin saloon was not mentioned during the long hours we waited for the brother to come.

The brother arrived late in the night while I sat with the other silent buckaroos around a fire in front of the bunk-house door. I conducted him to the bedside and told him the lad would never regain consciousness. He wept aloud, unashamed of his tears, and I left him there.

After some time he came out and joined the silent group around the fire and told his story.

The two brothers were the only children of an old and

respected couple living on a small ranch in Montana. Their mother had not been strong since the younger boy was born, far from town and the help of a doctor. The boys had been wayward and got into some minor trouble that caused them to leave the country between suns to keep out of the hands of the law. The old people, broken-hearted and disgraced, had with considerable difficulty and financial sacrifice patched up the offense and wanted the boys to come home to be with them in their old age. But the boys had never written, although their mother had spent money searching for them and had advertised in the newspapers,

The penitent and sorrowing brother stood silently for a moment, a tear on his cheek glittering in the light like a diamond as he stared into the fire. Then he said to himself, half aloud: "I wish to God I'd a wrote to her before this thing happened—I ain't got the guts to do it now."

Then all was silent. Far out on the range a wild stallion snorted his warning of danger to his band of mares, while from off in another direction the wail of a coyote floated faintly to us on the thin night air. The thoughtful buckaroos gazed into the fire in silence. Then Grizzly spoke.

"There ain't goin' to be any ridin' tomorry an' every one of you bygod wallopers that's got a mother has got to write to her. If there's any of ya that ain't got sense 'nough to write a letter I'll write tha damn thing fer ya."

Grizzly, like the others among the wildest of the reckless, harum-scarum buckaroos, had a lot of sentiment hidden away behind his rough exterior when circumstances brought his thoughts back to home and mother.

I met Grizzly occasionally after that night on the ranch,

sometimes in unexpected places. It was not long after that until the story of what happened in the log cabin got to the ears of the sheriff and he sent a deputy to question me. The country was settling up rapidly and there was talk of rounding up all the horse thieves and rustlers. So many new people were coming in who demanded more law and order.

A year or two later I happened to drop into the sheriff's office in the county seat, and there sat Grizzly, splendidly arrayed in handcuffs and an "Oregon boot." He had been brought in with some others in a general roundup and not on any specific charge. He seemed glad to see me and kept up his usual carefree banter, but it was a little forced. Knowing Grizzly would talk to me, the sheriff left us alone for some time.

Grizzly did not know how much evidence the sheriff had but did not think much could be proved against him in court.

"If they do send me up fer very bygod long, Doc, I might answer some of them questions ya asked me over in the Log Cabin that night when I wasn't as bygod drunk as ya thought I was," he began. "I might tell ya what happened to Conn, too, but you're the only bygod man in Chrise world that I'll ever tell a goddam thing."

"There's one thing you might tell me now, Grizzly. It won't make any difference to me whether you're sent up or not; it's just between you and me."

"What is it, Doc? Spit 'er out."

"Did the boys out at the butte intend to kill me the night I was out there?"

Grizzly was silent with a serious look on his face for a moment.

"Yes they did Doc," he said. "They was plannin' ta keep ya there 'till they was sure Tex would be all right an' they was well, an' then fix ya so 's you couldn't squeal. But when they seen ya an' sized ya up they knowed ya was a white man an' wouldn't squeal, an' I told 'em they was goddam right. I told 'em ya was all right or ya wouldn't a come out there on that — — — — of a trip through all that goddam weather. When they saw tha way ya fixed Tex up they thought ya was all right and backed out."

Grizzly was mistaken about how much could be proved on him. He was sent to the penitentiary for a long term. I regretted that I did not get to see him before he was taken away.

CHAPTER 12

Mr. and Mrs.—and the Doctor

THE exodus of so many people who followed the big payroll into the booming town of Redmond helped the housing situation. With fewer living in tents, sanitary conditions improved; consequently there was much less typhoid that second summer. In the spring there were only a few typhoid cases, scattered over a wide territory in the country; but soon after the flies reappeared they began to increase as summer went on.

The town was quiet as far as business was concerned, having reached the depth of business lassitude in midwinter, but an ever-swelling stream of new settlers was flowing in; the town was growing bigger than its boots.

Little Redmond was also growing rapidly; and since they had no doctor most of the time, I made frequent trips there.

But with the first warm weather of spring I took time off to go fishing and caught my first trout in Oregon waters the moment, almost, I made my first cast. The fish were ravenous enough to take any sort of fly that fell on the water and no skill was required to catch them. The fishing in the Deschutes River, and most of the lakes in the mountains, was unsurpassed any place in the world. I was very fond of fishing and hunting but was too busy to go often. I always expected to do more of it some time but did not realize how soon the wonderful fishing and hunting would be a thing of the past. I regret now that I did not take the time to do more of it.

As far back as I can remember, guns of any kind held a great fascination for me. When I was still a small boy I could not pass a hardware store window where guns were on display without stopping to gaze at them in deep fascination, until dragged away.

To compensate in a measure for my lack of opportunity to go hunting oftener, I always carried a six-shooter on my calls to the country and shot jack rabbits and coyotes from the buggy. Burning thousands of cartridges gave me enough proficiency to knock the jacks over as they ran off through the sage brush without slowing the team to shoot.

Strange as it may seem, there were people living within sight of the river who did not care to fish. My friend, the little minister with the long gray beard, was one of them. He went fishing a few times with borrowed tackle and made excellent catches, but could not see enough sport in fishing to warrant buying his own tackle. He told me confidentially, and with great seriousness, that he saw no great sin in fishing except for one thing. He thought it a gross deception to lead the poor fish to believe that a few gaudy feathers tied on a hook were a dainty morsel of food. Such rank duplicity was disturbing to him, although he had no compunction about eating fish caught in that manner.

John, the stable boy and hostler at the livery stable where I hired all my teams, was another who did not care to fish. John had left his home on the farm in the beautiful Willamette Valley and crossed the mountains to the cattle country of eastern Oregon, to become a cowboy and perhaps a cattle king eventually. But he could not obtain work on a cattle ranch as a cowboy without experience, and was obliged to take the job of barn boy and hostler.

One gorgeous night in June I drove home from a long trip to the country. The vast, mysterious desert, sleeping in the light of the full moon, with snow-capped peaks nearly a hundred miles away visible, and the presence of the Great Spirit hovering over all in silent benediction, gave the night a fascinating charm far beyond my powers of description.

As I drove up the main street toward the livery stable at the far end, the first clear light of the coming day was making the moon fade and painting the eastern skies in great masses of gorgeous coloring. As I drew near the stable I was suddenly awakened from my reverie and silent meditation by the harsh noise of a violent commotion just inside the open door. I stopped the team on the opposite side of the street to await developments.

Just outside the barn door stood the dilapidated wreck of a horse that had just had his saddle and bridle taken off. He was covered from head to tail with lather and sweat, plastered over with dust. His drooping head hung almost to his knees and showed bloody froth at the nostrils, and his sides and flanks heaved and thumped—he was about all in.

From inside the open door came the noise of a horse jumping about on the board floor and the loud angry voice of a man roaring out a stream of eloquent and blistering profanity. The clamor and cursing grew in volume and ferocity until a horse and rider suddenly exploded through the door into the street.

A tall, wiry cowboy sat gracefully in the saddle on a big, raw-boned, glass-eyed pinto that snorted, pitched, and bucked, as though he were possessed of seven devils. With his head down low and his ears laid back, the angry old pinto zigzagged from side to side down the street in a cloud of dust, going high, wide and handsome. While he buck-jumped, pitched, bucked, and sunfished in rapid-fire order, the tall buckaroo, with a derisive grin on his weather-bronzed face, sat "deep in the wood" with confident poise raking the angry old pinto with his spurs, flogging him along the side of his head and neck with his quirt, in an effort to turn him and head in the opposite direction. The buckaroo rode according to roundup rules and did not "pull leather," while the mad crazed old pinto plunged and bucked down the street two blocks before he was turned and headed in the opposite direction, then he jumped up onto the board sidewalk and bucked down the walk in front of the hotel, where he plunged into a wooden awning post that splintered with a loud crash. He bucked on down the walk past the livery barn and finally lit in a dead run down the road that led to the pass over the mountains. The hotel proprietor came running out with his bald head shining in the early morning light and shouted to me, "What tha hell's that goddam fool tryin' to do?"

"I don't know, but it looks to me like he had his heart set on leaving the country in a big hurry," I shouted back. And how that buckaroo could ride! He made one of the prettiest rides I ever saw, and I've seen many of the boys who won world's championships at the Pendleton Round-ups ride. No man could see daylight between him and the saddle.

I then drove into the barn where John, the barn boy, big-eyed and pale, stood with trembling knees.

"What's going on here, John?" I asked.

"I don't exactly know, Doc," he replied. "I was asleep up in the haymow when that orn'ry walloper come an' woke me an' said he wanted a saddle hoss. I told him there wasn't any saddle hosses in the barn, that these was all stage hosses and drivin' teams. Then he pulled that big gun o' his'n on me an' says, 'Git me a saddle hoss, kid, an' be mighty goddam quick 'bout it or I'll blow ye so full 'o holes yer hide won't hold ye.' I was scairt, an' I slid down the ladder an' grabbed the first hoss I come to, an' it was that mean old pinto they call Pankey. He's a wheel hoss in tha team that goes out this mornin'. What d' ya spose the boss 'll do to me fer givin' him that hoss?"

"Don't worry, John, the boss won't do anything to you. That bird had to have a horse in a hurry; he didn't care whose it was or how he got it."

"He sure didn't act like he was foolin'," said John. "I don't like these tough buckaroos up here in this country that's always packin' a gun around. These people up here in this country is different from down home, an' these orn'ry broncos is different—they ain't fit to be trusted. They're jest as liable to strike ya with their front feet as they are to kick ya with their heels. The country is different, the people is different, and the hosses is different. Jest cause some o' these here orn'ry broncs is broke to harness ain't no sign ya can ride 'em. They're jest as liable to buck tha first time ya put a saddle on 'em as they are the first day ya git a rope on 'em out on the range. I don't like 'em very much. I think I'll throw up this job an' go down home fer a spell, an' visit ma an' tha folks; they'll probably want me to help 'em at harvest anyhow. I don't like havin' a feller pull a gun on me that-a-way."

I helped John unhitch and we examined the wreck of a horse the fleeing buckaroo had ridden to the barn. He had been a good horse before that merciless ride. We washed the dust from his mouth and bloody nostrils, gave him a few swallows of water, and put a blanket on him. He wore the brand of a big cattle outfit whose nearest ranch was about a hundred and fifty miles away.

Who the fleeing buckaroo was, where he came from, or where he went, I never learned. Whoever he was he was a superb rider.

John remained a little jittery for a few days, then quit his job and went home to "visit ma and the folks" and never came back.

Among the new settlers who came to Bend that summer were Mr. George W. Hall and family, from Colorado. The family consisted of Mrs. Hall and five children, three boys and two girls. Mrs. Hall was a nurse. She was not a graduate of a nurses' training school, but she had worked as a practical nurse under some of the leading doctors of the West. She was one of those rare individuals born to be a nurse, energetic, hard-working, sweet-tempered, level-headed and kind-hearted, and she loved nursing.

The family took a house with more room in it than they required for themselves, and some of the rooms were made ready for patients. It would have required some stretch of the imagination to call it a hospital, but it was a place where a few patients could be taken care of, and was in reality the beginning of the town's first hospital. We did not have all of the equipment that even a small hospital should have, but Mrs. Hall knew how to get along with little, and her whole heart and soul were in the work, and that is what counts. She probably fitted into the situation better than a graduate nurse who had been accustomed to having every facility to work with. At any rate it was a place where a little surgery could be done by converting the kitchen into an operating room, and women could come to, from far away, to be confined. The place was soon filled with patients, and it was only a short time until we did not have enough beds.

There were many people coming into the country to file on timber claims in the vast pine forests outside of the reserves. Any citizen of the United States was entitled to file on one hundred and sixty acres of timber, to which he could secure a title in a few months, at a total cost to him of five to six hundred dollars. As soon as he secured a title to the timber, he could sell it to one of the big lumber companies for from twenty-five hundred to four thousand dollars cash. The active timber buying began to put a lot of outside money into circulation and my collections soon began to pick up a little. Collections had been so low for the preceding two-year period, during a part of which time the bank had been closed, that I did not take in enough cash from practice to pay expenses. But with the capital I had been so lucky to get during the first few months of practice, I made a lot of money in real estate and timber deals.

Thirty years ago the family doctor was usually the first man the average person turned to for advice and sympathy in time of trouble. He was usually the one best qualified to give advice, as he knew more about his patients, mentally, morally, and physically, than anyone else. An intimate relationship existed between doctor and patient, one founded on trust. It was and still is the finest thing I know. There has been nothing else exactly like it in the world, but it is likely soon to disappear. The tendency toward the regimentation of medical practice as we find it today in clinics, health and hospital associations, and in politically controlled hospitals, tends to destroy it. It has already been completely destroyed in all the principal European countries, where various systems of socialized medicine have gone into effect. Under all systems of socialized medicine the patient becomes a number instead of a human being.

A great clamor has been raised in this country for socialized medicine, but the American Medical Association has strongly opposed such a move. The question of furnishing the under-priviledged and indigent with medical care is a problem the medical profession has studied for centuries. At the present time there are three hundred plans being tried out in different parts of the United States. A system that will work in one location is entirely wrong in other parts of the country where conditions are different; no one system will be satisfactory for all. In addition to these three hundred different plans that are being tried in various localities, the doctors of the country are now donating without cost a million dollars in medical services every day. The American Medical Association has given careful study and consideration to all the various systems of socialized medicine now in use in all the principal European countries and strongly advises this country against adopting any of the plans here.

I had not practiced long before people began coming to me for advice in their marital difficulties. Being both very young and unmarried, it was a novel sensation to have older married people ask for my advice in their matrimonial troubles. I hesitated about giving such advice but soon found it useless to try to evade it.

One day a little, rosy-cheeked, blue-eyed, fair-haired farmer, weighing perhaps a hundred and twenty pounds, came to the office with his right arm broken between the wrist and elbow. He said he had been kicked by a horse. He was very self-important, pompous, and lofty in bearing, and strutted like a bantam rooster.

After the arm was well he came back to the office to ask my advice about his marriage problem. He told me his arm had been broken by a blow from his wife with a stick of stove wood. He told me a long story of his side of a marriage disruption, and impressed me as being honest and honorable. I was inclined to believe his story, but reserved advice until I could hear the other side of it from his wife.

He had always intended to marry and raise a family, but it seemed that the girls who interested him were not much impressed with him, and the years flew by until he was fifty and still a bachelor. In desperation he began correspondence with a matrimonial bureau and eventually drew a prize package from the wooded hills of Kentucky.

The prize package had slightly misrepresented herself in her letters and did not come up to expectations, but even so he wanted to keep her.

A few days after our interview, he called me in great agitation and asked me to hurry out to his farm eighteen miles from town. His wife was having a "spell" with her heart.

I found the wife lying on the bed with all her clothes on, apparently unconscious. Four neighbor women were tip-toeing around the room, speaking excitedly in whispers, with anxiety and fright written on their faces.

The patient was a big, coarse, mannish-looking woman, with black hair, a florid complexion, and a good start for a mustache on her upper lip. With her large hands, big feet, and well-developed muscles, I judged she would weigh about two hundred pounds, dressed. She was lying on her back with her eyes closed tightly, her head drawn backward, her jaws firmly set, and all her muscles tense. The poor frightened little husband paced the floor in the kitchen, while two neighbor men tried to comfort and encourage him.

One of the neighbor women told me the patient had been as well as usual all day until she got into a heated argument with her husband in the evening, when she suddenly screamed and fell to the floor unconscious. Another neighbor and his wife happened in a moment later.

By combining forces and strength, the husband and three neighbors managed to lift her onto the bed without the use of a derrick. They dashed cold water in her face, held ammonia and smelling salts to her nose and prayed, but when she did not "come to" I was called.

Her pulse was strong, smooth, and regular, and her pupils reacted normally to light. Her respiration was even, but quiet and barely perceptible, much like that of the opossum when feigning death.

I sat down by the bed a moment to think what I would give her to make her relax quickly and "come to." The women in the room concluded from my actions that the case was hopeless. They gathered about me and asked in excited whispers if there was any chance for the patient to recover. I assured them she would be much alive in a very few minutes.

I asked for a glass of water and a teaspoon. From my medicine case I concocted a vile mixture of ipecac and lobelia, either of which will produce violent vomiting and relaxation. Then I added some nux vomica and capsicum for a fillip.

When I started toward the bed with a teaspoonful of the mixture, a neighbor woman spoke up quickly.

"Oh, Doctor, she can't swallow!" she exclaimed, "We've tried to give her brandy." I said nothing but went on.

I inserted my little finger between her lips, pulled her cheek out away from her teeth, and poured the horrible concoction into the corner of her mouth.

She did not want to swallow it but did not dare spit it out, as that would have shown she was conscious. I sat down by the bed to await developments.

She held the concoction in her mouth as long as she could—at last I saw her slyly swallow it. I knew the fireworks would soon start.

In a moment the florid cheeks began to blanch and the tense muscles to relax. Then she suddenly flopped over on her side with a moan and a loud whoop, and began to vomit violently.

"Oh my gawd, I'm tabaccer sick! Oh gawd, I'm so sick," she moaned, while she continued to vomit and spew, and then retch and gag, after her stomach was empty. She was conscious and thoroughly relaxed. The hoodwinked and badly frightened little husband was called outside of the house and the case explained to him.

When he understood that his wife had purposely thrown the "spell" to frighten him and gain sympathy, he was mad all over. He was all for going into the house and telling her just what he thought of such dishonorable business. I advised him to think it over until morning, however, and reminded him that she was almost twice his weight, that she was of a belligerent disposition, and that she had already broken his arm. The thought then occurred to me that it might be a good idea for me to go home before she completely recovered from the vile dose I had given her.

As I was about to leave, one of the neighbor women asked what should be done if the patient had another "spell."

"If she shows the slightest symptom of another 'spell' coming on, give her another dose of the medicine immediately," I said.

"Oh fer gawd's sake, Doc, don't give me any more of that medicine; it's the most gawd-awful stuff I ever tasted in all my borned days," she moaned.

A few days later she came to the office for treatment for toothache, and I heard her side of the story of marital incompatibility.

She had represented herself to her husband to be a virgin, but admitted to me that she had been married twice before. He sent her a ticket to Oregon, but she would not have the marriage performed until he promised to deed her a one-half interest in the farm at the end of six months, provided the marriage was mutually satisfactory.

She was soon convinced the marriage could not succeed. Her husband was much older than she and had lived a life of celibacy so long that his virility was deficient. She knew what a normal man should be like, but could not tell him why she was dissatisfied without letting him know she had been married before.

She thought she was entitled to a half interest in the farm for giving up her home and making the long trip to Oregon, and tried to coax him to give it to her before the six months. When coaxing failed she resorted to force. She intended to go back to Kentucky as soon as she got the deed.

The next time the husband came for advice he admitted his deficiency with considerable embarrassment, adding that he was completely cured of matrimony. I tried to convince him that he might yet have a successful marriage with one nearer his own age and virility. I told him he had simply over-estimated his capacity and bitten off too big a chunk of femininity.

Argument and hostilities continued until the lady was finally induced to relinquish all claim to an interest in the farm for a cash payment and a ticket back to Kentucky.

That case was only the beginning of my career as a referee and adviser in unsuccessful marriages. Eventually, I knew the inside history and all the sordid details of nearly every marriage disruption in the community.

An attractive married woman of thirty came to me for treatment, complaining of nervousness, insomnia, loss of weight, and a whole train of symptoms as long as an Alaska sled track. She was refined, intelligent, and well educated, and had been a school teacher.

A careful examination did not reveal any organic trouble, and I asked her to tell me frankly why she was so despondent and unable to sleep. She said it was because her husband did not love her any more and then told me all about her troubles. She seemed to think I should be able to outline a course of procedure for her to follow that would revive her husband's lost affections, just as one might expect to reanimate a sleepy old tom cat with a dose of catnip.

Her husband had been so much in love with her at the time of their marriage that he gave up traveling on the road and went into business so he could spend more time at home with her. Then he began cooling off.

Their tastes were congenial, they got along well together, and enjoyed each other's company. They had never quarreled until a short time before when she accidently found a love note from a charming young widow in his possession. They had a fight then and had occupied separate rooms since. She was heartbroken, dejected, miserable, and implored me to tell her what to do to keep him from the widow.

The wife was reared in a religious family and had been taught that sex was an indecent, degrading thing, not to be thought of or discussed by nice people. She thought love and passion were two separate and distinct things. She became engaged after her husband had courted her ardently for a year, but held the marriage off for four years, wanting to be sure that her love was entirely pure and of the highest order and not tinged with sex infatuation. She expected her husband to have the same kind of feeling toward her, entirely devoid of animal passion.

She had felt a little sexual emotion at the beginning of her courtship but suppressed it and continued to destroy it until at the time of marriage she was frigid and devoid of passion.

I guessed at once what the real trouble was and began to question her about her sexual relations with her husband. She was reticent, embarrassed, almost offended until she began to realize I was interested and wanted to help her. She finally grew frank and told me all I needed to know. While I sat silently thinking what suggestions to make, she remarked:

"I don't know why it has been possible for me to tell you all these things. I wouldn't tell them to Walter for anything in the world."

That gave me an idea. I suggested that she tell Walter several of the things she had told me, but she flatly refused. It would be so immodest—the very thought of it made her blush. I explained that if Walter had the proper information about her he would be able to cooperate in trying to develop her dormant emotions, and she would have another chance to make the marriage a success. She flatly refused to discuss such things with Walter, however, and left the office discouraged and in tears.

Grief and desperation finally drove her to broach the subject to Walter a few days later. She told him just enough to puzzle and confuse him, and he came to me for information.

Walter was a fine-looking man of thirty-five; sober, industrious, and successful. He had been deeply in love with his wife and could not understand why she had no passion for him, and rapidly lost his passion for her. He found in the widow what was lacking in his wife, and wanted a divorce so he could marry her. If his wife did not consent to a divorce he intended to continue his relations with the widow, who, he said, was in love with him. He was genuinely sorry the marriage was a failure, and above all things did not want to hurt his wife, but he was in love with the widow and couldn't help it. During the eight years he had been on the road he had done about as much philandering as the average but obviously had never come in contact with a passionless and frigid woman. He did not know there were such women until he married. He could not understand it.

I explained to him that different doctors who have investigated have discovered that a large number of all women are without passion at the time of marriage. Some place the number at twenty-five per cent, and some as high as fifty per cent, depending on the locality and class of women investigated. A conservative estimate would place the number at at least thirty-three per cent, and those estimates are correct, as they are based on the statements of the women themselves.

I told Walter his wife would probably develop into a better wife if he would cooperate with her properly, and suggested that he give her another chance, but he had lost his "taste" for her and was in love with the widow.

I had several talks with the wife after seeing Walter, and she finally decided it was useless to try to regain his lost affections, but she was horrified at the thought of divorce. She had been taught that divorce was a sin and prohibited by the Bible. We had a long discussion over it.

Personally, I cannot see why the divorce should be considered wrong and sinful. If it is love and not the marriage ceremony that makes marriage holy, there can no longer be a real marriage when love has flown. It may still be legal, but it is nothing more than legalized adultery. When two people tied together by a legal marriage ceremony cease to love each other, the sooner they separate and are divorced the better for both, physically, mentally, and morally.

From that concept it would naturally follow that a woman who marries a man for his money, or for a meal ticket, when she does not love him, is simply engaging in a form of legalized prostitution—as others have pointed out. She is only selling herself to one man instead of many, and does not violate the law. She has always seemed to me more sinful than the woman who carries on marriage relations with the man she loves outside the formality of a marriage ceremony.

The unhappy wife was shocked by my views on the divorce question but must have changed her mind later, as she divorced Walter on grounds of infidelity, and he married the widow. It was a calamity that the marriage of two such splendid people had to be a failure, but regardless of age, physical characteristics, mental attainment, or financial conditions, sex is the fundamental relation which determines the final outcome of all marriages, for better or for worse. Not until that fact is learned by everyone will there be more successful and happy marriages, and fewer divorces—regardless of laws, customs, or religion.

The marriage of Walter and the ex-school teacher was completely disrupted by circumstances beyond control when they came to me. But in some cases my advice and instructions helped to prevent a marriage from going on the rocks, and seeing those marriages succeed was ample reward for all the time and annoyance they cost.

There were cases in which frigid wives were not pre-

vented by ignorance and false modesty from being perfectly frank with their husbands, and one or the other
came to me for advice in time to prevent the marriage
from being a failure. The average man does not know
enough about a passionless woman to know how to aid
in her development without help.

If the husband with the frigid wife would only spend
enough time in caressing, petting, and loving his wife,
she would soon become more responsive. Many men do
plenty of wooing, spooning and petting during courtship,
but stop it after marriage. The proper sort of loving and
petting after marriage, if persisted in, will pay big divi-
dends in the warmth of affection returned.

A husband may not have sufficient virility or sexual
stamina to aid properly in the development of a cold
wife; or he may have the virility but not the patience,
forbearance or consideration needed.

There were cases where a first marriage was a failure,
but a second one on the part of either or both of the prin-
cipals successful. I knew one woman who had nervous
prostration as the result of her first marriage who was
entirely cured by her second.

She was educated, good looking, intelligent, and physically perfect at the time of her first marriage. She married
a man much older than herself who was considered well-
to-do, handsome, and in all ways desirable. He gave her
comfort, some luxuries, and treated her with respect and
consideration. She was conscientious and did her best to
make a success of the marriage, but could not do so because they were sexually mismated. She had not been
deeply in love with him, but, attracted by his wealth and
position, she had yielded to the encouragement of her

family and come to believe she thought enough of him to marry him. Soon after the marriage she became ill and discouraged, and within eighteen months was a nervous wreck. Her husband finally gave her a divorce, but her health remained poor for a year.

Then she fell in love with a young lumber-jack, twenty years younger than her first husband. He was her inferior, socially and culturally, and in moderate circumstances financially. He could not give her the luxuries and comfort to which she had been accustomed, but he was an upright, industrious fellow. They lived on a homestead in the woods; she worked hard and lived plainly; but they were perfectly mated and she was happy and contented. She regained her health, raised two fine boys, and often told me how happy she was and how well she felt, all because she was properly mated with her husband.

My experience with marriage misfits has convinced me that if the proper sexual relationship exists between man and wife, nothing else matters very much.

I had for a patient an intelligent, attractive nurse, who married an uncultured man of foreign birth, a man who could not even provide a comfortable living for her. He was kind and considerate, but lazy, homely, uncouth and slovenly in his appearance. She made most of the living nursing, fought tooth and nail for her husband when occasion demanded, and worked hard as his willing slave and cheerful drudge, and told me she was happy and contented, all because he was a real man and they were perfectly mated. I took care of her when she had a miscarriage from over-work, when they were living in a little shack without conveniences and she was cooking for a crew of men. I did not hear a word of complaint from her, just a little disappointment at losing the expected baby and at being too sick to go on with the cooking. Her case is by no means unusual.

I was asked for advice in some cases of marriage failures that were not due to any deficiency or lack of development in the wife, but to the lack of virility in the husband. They were cases in which the husband had remained entirely continent and had practiced rigid suppression of sexual function for too long a period until his potency had been destroyed to some degree.

My experience with marriage failures has convinced me that the only way to decrease the vast number of marital catastrophes and divorces is to change our ideas, laws and customs in regard to the sex problem. Marriage is not a religious or moral question, but one of biology; and it is far more rational and sensible to consider the sex problem from a biological standpoint than from a religious or moral one. It is neither indecent, degrading nor immoral, and it should be studied and discussed openly and intelligently. It is a subject the youth of the country should be instructed in, one every girl should know about and understand at the time of her marriage. There is much evidence on every hand today, however, that people are beginning to take a more sensible view of the sex question than they did thirty years ago. When the time finally comes where sex problems will not be considered too indecent or delicate to learn about and young people are taught what they should know about the origin of life, there will be more happy marriages and fewer divorces.

CHAPTER 13

Complaints Real and Imaginary

AFTER our hospital, under the auspices of Mrs. Hall, got going, I found it a great convenience, especially in surgical cases. Her energy and enthusiasm never slackened, and with the help of her family she did an astonishing amount of work.

The time soon came when we did not have enough beds; but the man who owned the house was induced to build another like it on the adjoining lot. In order to keep the little hospital going I frequently treated some patients without cost if they would just pay for their hospital care. Some of them appreciated the accommodation; others did not.

When I think back over all the people I have worked for—and worried over—without pay, my thoughts always revert to the old couple who lived on a rocky forty-acre tract of irrigated land about two miles from town.

When the old man, who was a machinist by trade, became too feeble to work because of diabetes, his doctor in North Dakota sent him to the milder climate of Oregon so that he could be out of doors more. Coming to Oregon did benefit him in some ways, but the diabetic condition steadily progressed since there was no insulin then to stay its progress.

One day he dropped a stick of stove wood on the second toe of his left foot, and diabetic gangrene developed from the bruise. I was called to his home then for the first time and met his good wife. She was old, wrinkled, very homely, but she had a beautiful character and a heart of gold.

I told the old people the toe must be amputated and suggested that the old man ride back to town with me and enter the hospital. They hesitated because of the expense, as they had very little money, but I told them I would give the old man whatever treatment he required without charge, if they would pay whatever they could on the hospital bill. Mrs. Hall was a real humanitarian and sometimes gave hospital care to deserving people who could pay no more than the actual cost of their board.

The leave-taking of the old couple reminded me of the first parting of newlyweds. After a protracted farewell and affectionate kiss the old lady came and laid her hand on my shoulder.

"Please be careful of my old man; you know he's all I've got in the world," she said. Then she went back to her man and told him goodbye all over again.

The toe was amputated but the incision would not heal because of the diabetic condition. A few doses of insulin would have made the incision heal promptly, but insulin had not yet been developed. After trying in vain for weeks to get the incision to heal, I decided to amputate the foot higher up where the circulation was more abundant.

The whole foot was amputated and the stump was dressed twice a day for months, and every known means was used to make it heal, but without success. The old man remained in the hospital during all of that time, and the old lady trudged the two miles to the hospital every day, bringing him wild flowers, walking back over the dusty road each evening.

Sometimes, when I could, I took the old lady home in the buggy, pretending I had to go on a call that would take me by her place. She would not allow me to make a special trip on her account if she knew it. When the stump, after the second operation, had been dressed twice a day for many weeks, diabetic gangrene appeared in the wound and became so extensive that a third operation was necessary. This time the leg was amputated just below the knee. For a while the stump was dressed every eight hours, and I did every dressing I possibly could myself. After endless care and infinite patience it finally healed. It was just a year to the day from the time of the first operation before the leg was dressed for the last time.

The next day I drove the old man home to the little shack on the rocky forty, and was repaid for my trouble when I witnessed his homecoming. The old lady rushed from the house as he climbed out of the buggy and took a few steps on his crutches. They clasped each other in close embrace for a long time, and stood in silence, the old man standing on his good leg with his head bared while she held him close, with quivering lips and the tears streaming down her face.

As the old man's strength returned he made himself a wooden leg and was soon strong enough to walk to my office. Then for a whole year he was fairly well, except for the diabetes, and the two old people were just as happy as two children at a picnic.

I can see them now strolling down the dusty road hand

in hand, he stumping resolutely along on his wooden peg, she smiling proudly by his side. Then the old man developed a huge carbuncle on the back of his neck. The old lady did not want him to go to the hospital if it was not necessary—she wanted to be near and care for him. I was a little afraid his time had come when the carbuncle appeared, but with her constant and tender care he recovered, though the suffering sapped his vitality alarmingly.

It was not long, however, until an even larger carbuncle came that covered the whole back of his head and neck, with many smaller ones all over his head, neck and face which rapidly coalesced into one huge, hideous, repulsive-looking mass. I knew that was the beginning of the end, and I told the old lady as I had promised I would. It was pitiful to see her breaking heart when she was told, but she was wonderfully brave and was all smiles and the picture of cheerfulness when she was in the sick room with him. I kept him under the influence of morphine to soothe his suffering and often wished I could give him a dose that would put him to sleep forever. After weeks of suffering he died. The old lady made a brave fight up to the last, but she was completely tired out from her long hours of work and was almost prostrated with grief.

I did not see her for several months after her husband died and supposed she had gone back to her only relative, a brother in North Dakota, but one day a neighbor woman brought her to the office. She had sold her cow, chickens, and everything else on the place that would bring a little money, and had scraped up enough to buy a ticket back to North Dakota. She was leaving on the stage at daylight the next morning, and had asked her neighbor to bring her to the office so she could thank me for what I had done for her—I had never sent her a bill. She told me simply and sincerely how much she appreciated all that I had done for her, how sorry she was for not having the money to pay me, but said she would always remember me in her prayers, every night and every morning.

Her thanks were so sincere and her gratitude so genuine that it touched a spot in my heart money could never half way reach. Of all the people I have treated without pay, she is the only one who ever went out of the way to thank me for it. Her little act of courtesy is one tiny bright spot that still softly lightens my recollections of those busy days.

Fate decrees that it is not the pleasant things that stand out most vividly in the doctor's recollections of the past. To save a human life, either by quick thought and action, or by long toilsome effort, brings a thrill of satisfaction at the time, but it is soon forgotten. To be entrusted with the responsibility of a human life when the patient is suffering with an incurable disease—such as diabetes was at the time of the old machinist's death—is heartbreaking, and an unforgettable experience. Every doctor hopes to save enough money to enable him to study, do research work, and take post-graduate courses, in order to learn how to avoid such experiences.

I was fully aware of my limitations as far as knowledge and experience were concerned, and constantly felt the need of post-graduate study. I was so busy with the large territory I had to cover that there was no time for study. For two years following the removal of the payroll to Redmond, collections from city practice had been so poor that I could not make anything from practice. But with

the constant stream of new settlers pouring in, real estate
was steadily rising in value and scarcely a month passed
that I did not make some money in a real estate deal. I
kept all my capital invested for a time and then began
putting money in the bank for a post-graduate course.

But time was slipping rapidly by, and I was beginning
to be puzzled and worried to know how, and where, I
could get someone who was trustworthy to take my place
while I was away taking a course. Several doctors had located in Bend, but no one of them had stayed more than a
few months, and there was no one of them I would have
wanted to trust with my practice. During my first four
years in Bend, six different doctors came to locate, but no
one of them stayed more than six months. More than half
of the time I was the only doctor in town.

It was interesting to observe the reactions of different
people to a new doctor. Many who owed me a bill they
did not expect to pay consulted the new man. I was
usually glad to be rid of them for a time, and it gave the
new man something to do. The chronic neurasthenics
usually consulted every new doctor who came to town
with the hope that they might at last find someone
smart enough to agree with their own diagnosis of the
case or one who would at least agree that their case was
serious. Any doctor who would do either was sure to win
their gratitude and patronage.

Every community has its full quota of neurasthenics,
and most of them are women. They are usually a greater
trial and tribulation to the small-town doctor than to the
general practitioner in the city, as the city doctor can
refer them to a specialist and be rid of them, but there
are no specialists in the small towns. Most of the troubles

of neurasthenics are largely imaginary and spring from
a background of fear, but many really suffer considerably,
mentally and emotionally. Sometimes mental anguish is
harder to bear than physical pain, and such patients are
truly deserving of sympathy and relief from their suffering. But sympathy misdirected and without understanding will only do harm. What the doctor must do in order
to help is to find out what the primary cause back of the
trouble is and then try to eliminate it. That requires time,
patience, discernment, and understanding. It's a big
order.

Every neurasthenic has an endless list of complaints
and symptoms, and the doctor cannot begin to make an
examination until he has listened patiently to a recital of
the entire list. Then he must convince the patient that he
is really interested in her case and will do his best to help
her. He must gain her complete confidence before she will
truthfully answer all his questions and lay bare her real
desires and emotions. When there is a history of obscure
illness lasting over a long period of time, with a long list
of symptoms and complaints and no organic lesion to account for them, it is pretty certain that the patient is a
neurasthenic. Neurasthenic complaints usually have their
beginning with some disturbance or aberration of the
fundamental emotions of biologic urge—fear, love, hate, or
grief. If the neurasthenic patient can be made to understand that her illness had its beginning with a disturbance
of some of these emotions, she will usually tell the doctor
enough to put him on the right track, provided he has her
confidence.

Fear is nearly always a major factor in causing neurasthenic complaints. Hundreds of thousands of women live

in constant fear and dread of cancer, which sometimes amounts almost to a phobia. Yet there are many of them who will not go to a doctor for an examination in time to prevent a tragedy because they are afraid the doctor might tell them they actually had a cancer. When such a patient has a little pain that is not readily accounted for she imagines she has a cancer, and the element of fear at once asserts itself. The resulting emotional strain begins at once its demoralizing influence on the bodily functions, and a neurasthenic condition has its beginning. Deranged and impaired functions, if continued long enough, can in time produce organic changes.

Hate and jealousy are sure to produce emotional strain that will wreck a woman's nerves and make her look old and wrinkled before her time. Fortunate indeed is the woman who can put jealousy aside and keep hatred out of her mind.

Grief, especially suppressed grief, is a very potent and one of the most difficult of all the causes of ill health the doctor has to deal with. It is also one of the most difficult for the patient to overcome. Medical treatment is of no value in such cases; it requires time, patience, understanding, and properly directed sympathy.

The most frequent cause of neurasthenic complaints in married women is disturbances of the sexual functions due to sexual mismating between husband and wife. When it is remembered that self-preservation is man's strongest emotion or instinct, and reproduction is the second strongest, it may be readily understood why disturbances of the functions of reproduction cause so much trouble.

It required some time for me to come to the realization

that people with imaginary ills really do suffer, sometimes, more than the patient with an organic disease.
After I had been annoyed by a few such patients long
enough, and had no specialist to refer them to, I decided
that the only relief for me was to get down to brass tacks
and find out what was back of all their troubles. After
considerable work and worry I did unravel the etiology
of some of the cases, and was then able to be of some
help.

My third summer in Bend was rapidly coming to an
end and I still had no definite plans for a post-graduate
course when Lady Luck smiled on me once more.

One evening in late August I walked into the dining-
room of the hotel and noticed several strangers there who
had just arrived on the mail stage. One face looked
vaguely familiar and I took a closer look. I recognized a
former classmate at the University of Missouri, Dr. Barney
Ferrell, whom I remembered as the president of our
freshman class. He recognized me at once and was just
as much surprised to see me as I was to see him since he
had no idea I was in Oregon.

We had left the University at the same time; he to go
to Northwestern at Chicago while I went to Cincinnati,
to finish our medical schooling. After graduation he went
back to Illinois and located in his home town where his
father was a retired physician. Each summer he left his
practice with his father for a few weeks while he attended the regular annual meeting of the American Medical Association, after which he took a vacation trip. After
the Association meeting that year he went to the Pacific
Coast and came up into central Oregon just for the novelty of the stage ride of a hundred miles. He intended to

go back home the following morning, but he stayed on with me for a week.

During his visit I made plans for my post-graduate course, and he agreed to come to Bend the following year and take care of the practice while I was away. He also planned to return to Illinois after I came home, sell his practice there, and come back to Bend with me. The new railroad was expected to start construction in a year or two and we knew the town would be too large for one doctor by the time the road was built. Railroad rumors were flying thick and fast that summer, the large lumber companies being actively engaged in buying up the small tracts of pine timber, preparatory to building big saw mills as soon as the railroad arrived. The little town was growing rapidly and beginning to boom again. The summer passed quickly and the signs of fall began to appear.

The cattle and sheep were beginning to trail through town on their way from the summer ranges in the mountains to home ranches and winter ranges. The Indians trekked through on their way to the fall deer hunt in the mountains, sometimes a lone buck driving a dozen or more unloaded pack ponies or a whole family or two on their ponies, with a larger drove of pack ponies. They would all come back in the late fall loaded with jerked meat, deer hides and smoke tanned buckskin. On the return trip they would camp on the river near town a few days while the squaws sold big buckskin gauntlet gloves, or moccasins ornamented with beautiful colored bead work, for fifty and seventy-five cents a pair. The bucks often sold venison to the townspeople. A smoked ham from the big mule deer sold for from twenty-five to seventy-five cents.

A number of white men also went deer hunting that fall, the first time many of them had been particular enough to do their hunting in the open season—a sure sign the country was becoming civilized.

Among the hunters was a young tenderfoot from the Middle West who went on his first deer hunt to Crane Prairie, a beautiful mountain prairie on the river, fifty miles above town. Abundantly armed with a high-power rifle, hunting knife and automatic Colt six-shooter, which he carried in a holster on his belt, he rode a young bronco that was not very well broken. The prairie was still full of wild range cattle on summer range, with a crew of buckaroos camped at one edge of the prairie riding herd on them.

The lad rode forth one fine morning down a dim road along the edge of the prairie to the buckaroo camp and turned off into the thick pine timber. About a mile in the timber he came on the fresh trail of a bear. Most horses are thrown into a panic by the sight or scent of a wild bear, and the lad's young bronc was no exception. He started to bolt but the lad held him; then he began really to buck.

The first few jumps loosened the safety catch on the automatic six-shooter and it began discharging into his right thigh, one bullet striking the bone. Fortunately the empty cartridge from the second shot caught in the ejector and jammed the gun so it could not discharge again. The next buck threw the lad and he lit on his hands and knees. The fall broke the right thigh bone in a long oblique fracture extending the full length of the shaft of the bone. The bronc then bolted from the scene, taking the rifle, which was in its scabbard slung on the saddle, with him.

Retaining his wits and nerve in the midst of disaster, the lad wrapped his belt twice around his leg at the upper end of the fracture and buckled it tightly. He then bound the leg firmly at the lower end of the fracture just above the knee, with his big red bandanna handkerchief. That enabled him to crawl on his hands and the sound knee, and he started for the buckaroo camp, hoping to reach it before dark. It would have been more considerate of the bronc if he had tossed the lad up into the branches of a nearby tree where he would have been out of reach of prowling bears.

He worked his way slowly and painfully toward the edge of the prairie, with the blood dripping from his wounded leg leaving a trail behind. He at last saw the light of the open prairie filtering through the remaining trees at the edge of the forest and thought he would soon reach aid, but a terrible peril suddenly confronted him. He heard the loud, savage bellowing of a wild range bull and, peeping cautiously around the foot of a tree, saw the infuriated bull out on the edge of the prairie, less than a hundred yards away. Wild range cattle become excited and infuriated by the smell of blood, and this old bull had caught the scent of the blood dripping from the lad's leg.

Roaring and bellowing savagely, his eyes rolling wildly, his tongue lolling out its full length, he charged about searching for an unseen foe. He charged up toward the edge of the forest, lowered his head, shook his horns, began pawing the ground ferociously while his erect tail waved challenge and defiance high in the air over his back.

The sight of the infuriated bull made the lad's heart sink. He did not know what to do; but he was determined not to give up but die fighting. His first impulse was to climb a tree, but he realized at once that it would be impossible to do so with his broken leg. When he started to turn back to go deeper into the woods, he saw a new peril confronting him, and his blood ran cold.

Just a short distance away, snuffing along on the trail of blood, was a big brown bear. The old bear had struck the trail in his rambles and so of course followed it.

With the infuriated wild bull in front of him, the blood-thirsty old bear advancing from the rear, the lad was on the spot. Fortunately he had good lungs and he put them to work.

He yelled at the bear to frighten him away, but the old bear did not shoo worth a cent. The sight of a man down on all fours yelling at the top of his voice was such a curious sight, and the smell of fresh blood was so enticing, that the bear simply stood there fascinated.

When the lad saw that the bear did not shoo away, all he could do was to shout for help. He must have yelled louder than the bull could bellow, for although the bull was between him and the buckaroo camp the boys heard him and hurried to the rescue. The bull was driven away and the old bear shuffled off through the woods.

The buckaroos made a stretcher with saplings of lodge-pole pine and a blanket, and carried the lad up to a forest ranger's cabin, about a mile above the prairie, where there was a telephone line running into town. The lad's father came after me late in the afternoon and we started for the cabin at once.

When we arrived at the ranger's cabin I found the lad

in pretty fair condition, considering all he had been through, and prepared him for the trip to town. I made a temporary splint from a light pine board about five feet long, which reached from under his arm to a little below the foot of the broken leg. His body and the fractured leg were strapped snugly to the board splint so there could be no motion in the fracture. He was then strapped to an improvised stretcher and we started to town a little before midnight. We arrived about the middle of the forenoon with the lad in good condition.

After a few months the fractured leg was as good as ever, but it was a long time before he went deer hunting again.

CHAPTER 14

Ills and Bills

ALL THE cattle and sheep had been driven down from the summer ranges. The Indians were trekking back to the reservation after the fall deer hunt. Raging snowstorms swirled around the mountain peaks. Countless thousands of wild duck and geese streaked southward across the skies, and hundreds of wild swan formed big wedge-shaped flocks higher up. It was fall.

With the first cold snap came an epidemic of colds, la grippe, or influenza as it is called now.

I was called to the home of Uncle Frank Nichols, one of the old pioneers living in Laidlaw, to attend him and Uncle Marsh Aubrey, another old-timer well along in his eighties, both with severe cases.

Uncle Marsh, one of the first stockmen to settle in eastern Oregon, was a veteran of the Mexican War, and some of the Indian wars of the Northwest. At one time he owned the largest and one of the best brands of horses on the range. But he had retired to a small irrigated ranch near Laidlaw.

I found Uncle Marsh lying on the lounge in the front room with his boots off, but wearing his best clothes and his wide sombrero. He had a severe head cold, a well-developed bronchitis, an abscess in each ear, and a temperature of 104. Pus was running from his ears and he was so deaf I had to shout to make him hear. He had an old chronic heart disorder with a loud, harsh murmur that sounded like an old thrashing machine in the midst of disintegration.

I told him he must go to bed for a few days and thought I had convinced him it was necessary. He had never had a doctor before and did not know there was anything wrong with his heart.

When I had finished with him I went into the next room and was examining Uncle Frank when Old Marsh came padding through the room in his sock feet.

"Hey! where are you going?" I shouted at the top of my voice.

"I was jest goin' to tha kitchen to git me a drink of water," Uncle Marsh replied.

"Well, you get back in there and lie down and I'll get it for you," I said. "You shouldn't be up at all with that rickety old heart of yours, and you shouldn't be padding around in your sock feet without your boots. If you don't go to bed and stay there, that bum old pump of yours will quit on you, and the first thing you know you'll wake up dead."

"You mean to say I'm liable to pass in ma chips?" the old man asked, with his hand cupped to his ear.

"Yes!" I yelled.

Uncle Marsh grunted, nodded his head, and went back to the lounge. I took him a glass of water. Before leaving the house I again cautioned Uncle Marsh to stay in bed a week and told him he might die if he did not do as I said.

Two days later I was returning from a long trip to the

country when I met the sheriff about forty miles from town.

"How about Uncle Marsh?" he asked. "Is he seriously sick?"

"No, not seriously," I replied. "He's in bed down at Uncle Frank's house with a severe attack of la grippe."

"Like Hell he is," the sheriff snorted. "He came into my office in the court house yesterday afternoon: 'Say Frank, that doctor over at Bend told me I was goin' ta die,' he says, 'an' I got a little business I want ya ta fix up fer me before I have ta cash in ma chips.'"

Unable to hear well, Uncle Marsh thought I had told him he was sure to die. He sneaked out of the house before daylight the next morning, saddled his horse, and rode forty-two miles to the county seat, with the temperature below zero. That would have been a hard trip on a well man, but apparently it did Uncle Marsh no harm. A week later he rode into town on his favorite saddle horse, seeming as well as ever. He lived several years after that and died on his ninety-sixth birthday.

After that experience I did not try to keep any more of those old pioneers in bed with a threat of death. I was afraid they might think of some unfinished business and make a forty or fifty mile ride to attend to it.

One splendid pioneer woman got out of bed when she was sick and went out into a blizzard to put some stock in the barn out of the storm, and lost her life because of it. She was the wife of a homesteader living on the east fork of the Deschutes River, twenty-eight miles south of town, well up toward the foothills of the Cascades where there was snow on the ground most of the winter.

Her husband and nineteen-year-old son spent the entire fall and winter trapping in the Paulina Mountains, while the plucky wife remained entirely alone to take care of the home and feed the stock. She was completely cut off from the outside world except for some neighbors on a cattle ranch on Paulina Prairie, a few miles away.

Her son was very fond of her, and sometimes came in from the trap line, the nearest part of which was twenty-five miles away, to visit her. The day before Christmas he brought her a beautiful silver fox skin and took her to a dance at a little community settlement twelve miles away, returning to his traps the next day.

She took a heavy cold at the dance and went to bed for a few days, but a heavy snowstorm and blizzard came up and it was then that she got out of bed and went out into the storm to put some of the stock in the barn. She almost collapsed before she could get back into the cabin.

The women on the cattle ranch became uneasy about her and drove over to visit on New Year's Day. They found her very sick with pneumonia, managed to lift her into their sleigh, and took her back to the cattle ranch with them. They attempted to call a doctor, but the telephone line had been blown down by the blizzard, and all the men of the ranch were out to look after cattle that were caught in the storm. The women did all they could for her, taking turns standing out by the road to hail the first traveler, but none came by.

When the men returned to the ranch, one immediately called me, while another started for the trap line on snowshoes to notify the husband and son. After a hard trip up Paulina Mountain, he found one of the trappers' cabins and left a note tacked on the door.

I received the call just after dark the day the blizzard

ceased, and started at once for the cattle ranch with a buggy and team of frisky broncs. The cold was intense, but I was dressed warmly, with big high-topped overshoes, angora fur chaps, fur overcoat and fur cap, and had plenty of robes.

The snow-hidden road ran southward from town, meandering through thick pine timber and increasing in altitude nearly a thousand feet in the first nine miles to Lava Butte, where the snow was nearly three feet deep. If it had been a few inches deeper it would have been impossible for the buggy to get through.

A mile or two beyond the butte I met a mail stage that had been snowbound for two days at a ranch a mile or two further on. Big pines were standing so close together on the right side of the road that I could not pass, so the stage driver turned out on his right. A few feet off the road the four stage horses went down almost out of sight in the snow, pulling the old stage down with them. I hurried on without waiting to see what happened. For a mile or two the stage had partially broken the road and it was easy to follow, but most of the way it was very difficult to tell where the road was, and I got out of it and into drifts many times.

My broncos bucked the snow heroically, but it was almost daylight before I got to the ranch. There I found the woman with a double pneumonia, slowly dying. In a short time her husband came in on snowshoes, after traveling through the woods all night. She did not recognize him, but she had been calling for her boy through all her delirium. The husband stood at the foot of the bed, gazing at his wife in a wide-eyed trance as if unable to realize she was dying. I gave her stimulants for an hour but there was no response.

A little after daybreak the dazed husband called me out of the house and begged me to keep his wife alive, if possible, until her boy could get there. While we were talking, the faint report of rifle shots sounded far away at the foot of the mountains and the man's face lit up.

"That's Benny; he's coming," he said.

We went back into the house and I heard the death rattle in the woman's throat. I gave her stimulants with no effect. The husband sat by the bed, holding the dying woman's hand, while the long anxious moments dragged wearily by; still the boy did not come. She became pulseless; the death rattle increased; the breathing became shallower; there was a spasmodic twitching of the face muscles, a little choke and gurgle, and she breathed her last.

I looked out of the window and saw the boy coming, swinging jauntily along on his snowshoes, his rifle under one arm and a roll of freshly killed skins on the opposite shoulder, with his dog, Terry, following his snowshoe trail. Small for his age, with his slight wiry build, he did not look more than sixteen. Flushed with the luck of his recent kill, there was a smile on his face. I went outside and stood by the door, waiting for him to come up. He smiled broadly when he saw me.

"Hello Doc, how's ma?"

"She just passed away a few minutes ago."

"Wha—wha—what did you say, Doc?"

"She's dead, Ben."

He stopped in his tracks, hung his head, dropped his

rifle in the snow and slumped to one side to let the skins roll from his shoulder. While the tears ran down his cheeks he raised his hands to his face and cried like a child. I stood there watching his slight frame shake and quiver with grief. Finally he checked his tears and raised his eyes to mine.

"God, Doc, why did she have to die? She never done nothin' wrong, an' she worked hard all her life. Why did she have to die?" he repeated with childlike simplicity.

Benny had been out on the line all the previous day, coming back to their trap-line cabin after dark. There he had found the note from his father about his mother's illness. He ate a hurried meal, then followed after his father to the ranch.

When he neared the foot of the mountain about daylight, he came on the tracks of three mountain lions and, reading the sign in the snow, saw where they had attempted to drive a deer into deeper snow so they could catch it; but the deer had eluded them. He did not turn aside to follow the tracks, but hurried on toward the ranch. A mile or two farther on he came on the lion tracks again, and his dog, Terry, treed one. He shot the lion and had just stooped over to skin it when the dog suddenly became excited, looking up into the tree above, and barking. Glancing up, the lad saw a huge lion crouched on a limb ready to spring. He quickly seized his rifle and fired just as the lion sprang. It fell dead at his feet, shot through the brain. He then remembered he had seen the tracks of three lions and began looking for the third. The dog soon treed it and Benny added its pelt to the other two.

While Benny went into the house I spread the skins out on the snow to examine them. The lion that came so near springing on him was a huge old tom with the largest and finest skin I have ever seen. The others were females, one medium sized and the other a little larger. He found their stomachs empty when he skinned them but all hides were in prime condition.

After some time Benny came out of the house and saw me admiring the big lion skin. He presented me with it and I had it mounted later to keep as a souvenir of the fruitless snowy trip.

As no one knew when the next mail stage could get through, I waited at the ranch while letters and telegrams were written for me to send to the dead woman's relatives back east, and to a married daughter in Portland.

The only tracks in the road when I went back to town were those I had made coming to the ranch, and those of the old mail stage. Some of my tracks were not exactly in the road. The bridge over Paulina Creek had no railing, and the snow drifted between the banks on top of the ice until it was level with the road. I had lacked only a few inches of missing the bridge in the darkness. The day was bright and still, but cold and crisp, and the snow on the pine boughs made the woods look like a forest of Christmas trees in fairyland. The old stage was still stuck in the drift where I had passed it the night before, but the mail sacks and horses had been taken away.

Calls to the section south of Lava Butte were the hardest of any I had to make. It seemed to me that in summer I was seldom called to that section, but just as soon as the first big snow came in the winter, the calls always came in thick and fast.

I did not mind physical hardship, however, as I was young and in first-rate physical condition from my athletic training for football and baseball in college. The most disagreeable part of practice to me was the financial and economic part. I thoroughly dislike making records and keeping books, and it is always distressing to me to have to ask anyone to pay his bill. I have always been a poor collector and suppose I always shall be.

I never asked anyone to pay a bill I did not know I had earned, and never intend to. Consequently when a patient kicks about the charge I feel like throwing the money right back at him. I may be too sensitive in that respect, but do not seem to be able to get over it. Sometimes it is a pleasure to make only a nominal charge to one who is deserving and appreciative, but the more you do for most people the more they expect and the less the appreciation. When a patient kicks out of sheer stinginess, it is very disgusting to me. Here's a case in point:

The first contact I had with the family was in treating the seventeen-year-old daughter through a siege of typhoid. The parents, especially the mother, were fussy, apprehensive, inclined to be critical of my services, and demanded more time and attention than were necessary. As soon as the girl recovered, her mother came to the office to pay the bill. She began by saying she hoped I would be as reasonable as possible, as they could not afford much of a bill. When I added the charges and told her the amount she almost fainted, so I cut the bill in half. She seemed to think that even that was too much. I noticed the family lived comfortably and even a little pretentiously, and discovered later that not only was the husband's business paying well but the mother had an income from a trust fund left from her father's estate.

Later the son and heir of the family had an attack of broncho-pneumonia and the whole family was near distraction. They kept me on the jump day and night, although the boy was in no danger at any time. When he was well the mother came to the office promptly to pay the bill. She brought a long tale of woe and poverty along with her check book, and again made a big fuss about the amount of the bill. I was thoroughly disgusted but gave her a big reduction.

The mother kept a stock of medicines and a thermometer in the house and treated the minor ills of the children in order to save a doctor bill. One night the youngest daughter, a pretty blue-eyed golden-haired girl of six, had a troublesome cough that was keeping the family awake. The mother got up to give her cough syrup but made a mistake in the darkness and got hold of a bottle of tincture of aconite. She gave the girl a teaspoonful of it—a deadly dose. The girl made a fuss about the cough syrup tasting so bitter and the mistake was discovered. The whole family was thrown into a panic and the mother was frantic.

Fortunately, I was only four blocks away, in the midst of a confinement, and some of the family knew about it. While the mother was having hysterics and the father was berating her for the mistake, the noble young son happened to come home from his evening of dissipation and had the presence of mind to sprint after me.

I got him onto a saddle horse that just happened to be standing idle at the house where I was and started him to the office at top speed for my stomach pump, while I sprinted to the girl's house. For some unaccountable reason he brought everything I sent him for and I had everything I needed for the case. While the mother raved and wrung her hands, and the father scolded her for making the mistake, and the balance of the family got in the way, I managed to get the little girl's stomach washed out and antidotes administered. While I was still busy with her, the husband of the woman I had deserted in the midst of her labor came and insisted that I return to her aid, but I did not leave the girl until she was out of danger, some time after daylight. The woman in labor had her mother and a practical nurse with her, and I had to take the chance that she would get through without me. The baby had been born two hours when I did get back to her, and the whole family was mad because I had left her to go through the hardest part of the labor alone.

When I told the little girl's mother she was out of danger, she seemed very grateful and was profuse in her thanks, and I supposed she would pay the bill without a kick. I had put in six or seven hours of hard and anxious work, had lost the fee I would have received for the confinement, and had made a whole family mad at me. I thought I would make the charge so reasonable she would pay it without making a disagreeable scene. The first of the month I sent her a bill for twenty-five dollars.

As soon as the stingy old girl saw the bill she made a bee line for the telephone.

"What is this bill for you sent me, Doctor—there must be some mistake," she said in caustic tones.

"It is for the night's work I did for you when I saved your little girl's life," I replied.

She said she knew it was a night call, and realized that doctors charged more for night calls, but she had never paid more than ten dollars for a night call—not even in a big city. She spouted on and on until I was thoroughly disgusted and interrupted her. I told her to send me whatever she thought saving her little girl's life was worth, and hung up. The next day I received a check for ten dollars. I was so furious that I tore the check up and vowed I would never do another thing for her.

The next time she called me, there happened to be another doctor in town, and I told her to call him; that I was too busy, and I continued to refuse each call she gave me.

She had a naevus, or birth mark, on her neck, in the form of an angioma (a small mass of tiny blood vessels), which formed an ugly red blotch on the skin. I had succeeded in obliterating a similar angioma on the face of a friend of hers after nearly a year of persistent treatment. The patient had been faithful in doing her part of it and had paid her bill every month, amounting in all to about a hundred and fifty dollars. The stingy old girl showed me her birth mark and asked if it could be obliterated, as Mrs. Smith's had been. I told her that I thought it could.

"Oh, that's fine," she said. "I'll give you fifty dollars if you'll take it away." She knew, of course, what Mrs. Smith had paid in her case.

"Oh, you're entirely too generous," I replied. "I wouldn't want to rob you like that. I might charge you twenty-five or fifty dollars for saving your little girl's life, but surely you wouldn't want to part with all of fifty dollars for a little thing like that, would you?" She never called or annoyed me again, and I was mighty glad to be rid of her.

One fine spring day Henry Miller came into the office, and seemed unusually light-hearted, friendly and affable. I supposed he wanted medical advice for some member of his family, but he seemed pleased to tell me they were all very well. He gave me a pressing invitation to come over to his ranch on the Metolius River, forty-five miles from town, for some fishing and a real German dinner cooked by Frau Miller herself. I was too busy to go that far away and was obliged to decline. Henry was visibly disappointed and insisted on my going regardless of business. He kept chatting on and on until I was becoming nervous because he was taking so much of my limited time. At last he got up to go, insisting that I must come to the ranch the very first day I could get away. When almost at the door he suddenly turned and faced me again.

"By de vay," he said, trying to appear as though the thought had just occurred to him, "vot should you do mit a fine horse vot got himselvf on de shoulder ge-kicked mit 'nodder horse, und it is all big upsvelled und he is lame already?"

I began to suspect a motive behind the dinner invitation, but questioned him about the injury and suggested treatment.

In a few days he was back with another pressing dinner invitation, but I was obliged to decline the second time. He stayed on and chatted a long time, telling about all the special German dishes Frau Miller would prepare for me, but did not mention the injured horse until he was leaving. I gave him directions for further treatment.

The third time he came I saved much valuable time by asking about the horse as soon as he came in. I gave him directions for more treatment and he left, without inviting me to dinner. The shoulder finally healed but the horse remained a little lame, so Henry traded him for a sound horse and a little cash to boot. If Henry had been honest and straightforward about wanting me to see the horse, I would at least have made an effort to go to the ranch, but as it was I did not try to arrange my business so I could go.

Every call to the Miller Ranch was a rush call, and I invariably found one of the children had been sick for some time. Frau Miller always attempted to treat the case to avoid the expense of calling me, and I was not sent for until the symptoms became alarming.

One midnight Henry sent a frantic call and I rushed to the ranch and found little eight-year-old Heinie choking with a diphtheritic membrane in his throat. I gave him a big shot of antitoxin and stayed at the ranch until he showed improvement. Before leaving I gave him a second dose that used up all the antitoxin I had with me, and there was none left to give little five-year-old Lena for a prophylactic to keep her from catching diphtheria from Heinie. I told the Millers that if Lena showed the least sign of illness they should call me immediately. I prepared a liberal supply of medicine for Heinie to take and returned to town. Heinie recovered before all the medicine was taken, and Frau Miller, with her usual thrift and economy, saved it.

Lena soon became ill, with symptoms like Heinie's, and Frau Miller gave her the medicine left from his case, instead of calling me as she had been told to do. Not knowing that it was the antitoxin that had cured Heinie, they thought the medicine would be sufficient. When the medicine was about gone, Henry came to town to transact a little business, and to get more medicine.

When Henry described Lena's symptoms, I told him I should see her at once instead of sending medicine. He hesitated about the expense, but finally told me to go ahead, and he would follow as soon as his business was attended to. I hurried out to the ranch and found Lena dead. She had apparently died of heart failure, caused by the toxins of diphtheria. I started home and met Henry about half way to town. He pulled up at the roadside and waited for me to stop.

"How is my leddle Lena?" he asked.

"Little Lena is dead, Henry," I said. "She was dead when I got there and there was nothing for me to do."

"Ach, mein Gott, my leddle Lena isch dead already. Ach, mein Gott, boo-hoo-oo-oo, boo-hoo-oo," he bawled. He continued to bawl away with energy and gusto, like a big Hereford cow that has lost her calf, when he suddenly stopped abruptly and sat up straight in his seat.

"Doç, you say you do noddings for Lena ven you got dere?"

"No, Henry, there was nothing for me to do then; you should have called me sooner as I told you to," I replied.

"Doc, how much you scharch me ven you do noddings?" he asked.

Disgusted with his mercenary grief, I blurted: "Just forty-five dollars, Henry, the regular fee of a dollar a mile," I said grimly.

That started him off bawling again, harder than before. He seemed to feel worse about the charge than about the death of his little girl; at any rate, he bawled harder.

I sat in silence, waiting for his grief to subside, but it did not slacken, and I interrupted his blubbering. I told him that inasmuch as he seemed to feel worse about the charge than about the death, I would knock off ten dollars. I thought he had bawled at least ten dollars' worth, anyhow.

"Ach, dot's fine, Herr Doctor!" he exclaimed. "Danks, danks, dot's sere goot." His tears stopped instantly and he smiled blithely. Having bawled away ten dollars of the fee, he seemed well pleased with himself and satisfied with his accomplishment. He was still smiling happily when he drove on toward home.

I would not have been so disgusted with the Millers' stinginess if they had not been so well-to-do. They had a good ranch, several hundred cattle, money in the bank, and some horses and sheep.

It seemed to be the well-to-do that were the stingiest, but it was the poor who had the most sickness and the largest families.

The Bollingbroke family was a typical example of the poorer class. They were English and Papa Bollingbroke was a nephew of the famous and illustrious Sir Richard Percival Marmaduke Bollingbroke, for whom he was named, but his wife called him just plain Dick.

Dick was a cook and barber by professions and, when he had money, a drunkard by occupation. He seemed to be very lucky in securing work, but as soon as he got a good job and began to prosper he usually got drunk and lost his job.

Mamma Bollingbroke was the wheel horse of the family team as far as working was concerned. She took in washing at the two tents she called home (there was no laundry in a hundred miles), or went to private homes to do it for four dollars a day.

They had five children when I met them first, and nine when I heard of them last. I officiated at the ceremonies when three new Bollingbrokes were ushered into this world of sorrow and sent their first wails of protest heavenward, and I did a vast amount of other work for them. Some member of the family was almost always sick or injured.

At one time the family moved to Redmond, where Dick secured the job of cooking at the hotel, and I thought I would be rid of them for a while. But it was not long before Dick sent a frantic call for me one dark night. Mamma Bollingbroke had taken a whole big bottle of laudanum with suicidal intent.

At that time it was twenty miles to Redmond by the old wagon road that meandered drunkenly through the thick junipers east of Forked Horn Butte, and the road was as rocky as it was crooked.

I made a record-breaking ride that night and nearly ruined a mighty good saddle horse, but I got there in time to pump out her stomach and save her life.

As financial worries were partly to blame for the attempt, and I felt a little guilty for compelling her to remain in a world that had treated her so harshly she wanted to leave it, I made no charge for the trip. After they moved back to Bend their bill grew so large that I stopped making charges altogether until Dick got a good job and told me with pride and enthusiasm that he was going to pay me for every call I made thereafter. Then the account began to grow again, regardless of Dick's good intentions. Dick carried the family pocket book and Mamma B. turned her earnings over to him.

Mamma B. was very proud of Dick because of his connection with the illustrious family and did not complain or chide him when he became despondent at being ostracized by his distinguished family and attempted to drown his sorrow in drink.

By some lucky turn of the wheel of fortune, Dick got a job as cook in an isolated logging camp on the other side of the mountains, and the job of assistant cook for his wife, with a good salary for each of them, and free board and housing for the family thrown in.

They moved away, to my financial gain, and I did not see them again, but received news of them from friends to whom they wrote.

In addition to cooking, Dick operated a barber shop on Sundays, with no competitor within forty miles over roads that were impassable in winter. With shaves at fifty cents and haircuts at a dollar, he soon had a sizable bank account, and no place to spend the money.

When I heard of their prosperity, I wrote Dick and invited him to pay a little on account, but received no reply.

Some time later news came from authentic sources that one of Dick's uncles had died in England and left him several thousand pounds. I then wrote again, and in time a letter came, but there was no check in it. In the letter Dick told me they had a new baby boy, the ninth baby and the only boy in the lot. According to the letter he was a prodigious youngster and they were extremely anxious that he should have a name befitting one of his great promise.

Dick wanted to name him after his illustrious dead uncle whom he thought was the greatest man in the world. But Mamma B. thought King Edward had Dick's uncle topped a little for greatness and wanted to name the baby after the King.

When a vote of the children was taken they all voted for me, and then a brilliant idea was born in the fertile brain of Dick. He would pass up the honor due his dead uncle, who had been a little stingy in his will anyhow, and name the baby after me if I would square the account he owed me and send a receipt in full. Unfortunately, they had forgotten the correct spelling of my given name. Along with the receipt he urged me to be sure and give them the correct spelling of my name so there would be no mistake. I felt greatly honored but was not inflated—not with money, at least—for when I studied the matter carefully, it was plain that I ranked as one of the three great men of the world, so far as the Bollingbroke family was concerned.

I thanked Dick for the great honor he had shown me but told him I preferred the cash. In order to show my appreciation, I offered to cut the bill in half for immediate payment. After that was paid, they might call the baby anything they liked. That was the last I ever heard from Dick. After a time I sent the bill to a collector in the nearest town to the camp.

Later the collector wrote that Dick had quit his job as soon as the first money came from England and that the family had gone to California for the winter.

In the spring I received a picture post card from some of the children, sent from Yellowstone National Park, which stated the family was taking in the sights on their way to England. A month or so later another card came from Quebec, just before the Bollingbrokes sailed for England.

Dick actually did inherit several thousand pounds, but he never sent me a cent.

CHAPTER 15

Busman's Holiday

My SECOND month of practice yielded me about nine hundred dollars in cash, and a large part of it was profit as there were no expensive serums and glandular products such as are in use today. The drugs in use then cost about ten per cent of the more effective remedies we have now. My livery bill was not large until after the typhoid epidemic got under way; then it soared into the skies. Living expenses and office overhead were comparatively cheap, but books, instruments, medical journals, society dues, and other equipment cost about what they do today.

The following two months were even better, with the result that I got together a little cash capital right in the beginning. I invested every cent immediately in real estate. It was almost impossible to buy a piece of property that did not rise rapidly in value. As soon as the big payroll was taken away, my collections began a steady decline, and almost reached the zero point in the depression of 1907. Land under the irrigation project was first selling at about fifteen dollars an acre, and I bought all I could pay for. A year or so later the price was advanced to about forty dollars an acre and I sold all but one forty-acre tract which I had fenced and cleared of sage brush and a little later sold for about sixty dollars per acre. I filed on a timber claim and proved up on it at a cost of about five hundred dollars, and about two years later sold it for twenty-five hundred. The money was reinvested in timber. At that time timber was a gilt-edged investment.

Although collections steadily declined, I kept the capital I was so fortunate to get in the beginning constantly at work, and soon began putting money in the bank for a post-graduate course.

During the business depression of 1907, the Governor of Oregon declared every day a legal holiday for many weeks, to prevent runs on banks over the state, many of which were heavily encumbered with frozen assets. When the holidays came to an end, the little state bank in Bend did not open for business, and all the money I had was in it. My chances for a post-graduate course looked very doubtful.

The president of the bank was not a banker but a timber man who was a close friend and a joint owner of real estate with me. He wanted to reorganize the bank and make a national bank out of it, and asked me to help him. I agreed, and we began checking all of the business of the bank since it started. I knew nothing about banking, but had had a course in book-keeping in high school. I was very busy and often out of town for twenty-four hours at a time, but every night that I was in town and not busy with a confinement, we worked on the books, sometimes all night. By the summer of 1908, the check was complete, and we were ready to reorganize.

After protracted negotiations, we succeeded in persuading five of the largest depositors to take stock in the bank and help in its nationalization. When they became interested, confidence was restored, and business began to improve. The big lumber companies were very active in buying timber, and most of the business went through the bank, and that brought it good revenue. I saw then that the bank would pay the depositors more than we had at first hoped, and I wrote Dr. Ferrell that I would be ready to go east for my post-graduate work as soon as he could come. He wrote back that he would come in three months. With the bank work and the busy practice, I was going a terrific pace but thought I could hold out three months longer. We applied for a charter for the National Bank, and began looking for an experienced banker to take stock and become its cashier.

There was very little paper money in circulation. An easterner occasionally came to town with a few bills of the higher denominations, but one and two-dollar bills were never seen, and the fives were scarce enough to be a curiosity. The westerner, especially on the frontier, demanded gold and silver; not that he did not have faith in the currency of his Uncle Sam, but he simply preferred the genuine article when it came to money. There were no pennies, and no articles in the stores were ever priced in odd cents. We had nickels and dimes in the bank, but the nickels were not counted or carried in the cash account. If one bought a two-cent stamp at the post office he was obliged to take his change in stamps. The interest rate on loans was ten per cent, and the borrower sometimes paid a bonus to get the loan. We were obliged to ship in large amounts of silver every two or three weeks and shipping silver was expensive.

When a recently arrived easterner was charged a quarter for a large sack needle, he remarked about the price being high.

"Oh, I'm giving you the needle," the merchant said, "the twenty-five cents is to pay the freight on it."

At the end of three months Dr. Ferrell wrote that he had been delayed by legal business and could not come until after the next term of court. The cashier for the new bank had arrived, but the charter had not come. In the meantime I kept working at top speed, and finally reached the point where I could not sleep. My hair was falling out and I was losing weight.

The failure of the old bank and taking stock in the new one took most of my cash, but I was determined to take the post-graduate course, even if it had to be a short one.

Reopening the bank and heavy timber buying by the big lumber companies put more money in circulation and helped collections a little. While waiting for Dr. Ferrell, I spent all the time I could trying to collect, and what with selling off property managed to get enough cash together to finance a six months' course.

I had intended to go to Europe for a year; the big clinics and universities in Berlin, Vienna and other European cities offered the best post-graduate courses in the world at that time. It was a keen disappointment not to be able to go, though I thought I would be able to manage it later. But the World War came soon and then it was too late. Since the war all the principal European countries have adopted socialized medicine and doctors from this country no longer go to Europe for study and post-graduate work; they can get better instruction and more advanced work at home.

Under socialized medicine, in addition to having twice as much sickness to treat, the doctors are required to do a large amount of book-keeping—filling out blanks in duplicate and triplicate, making out reports and entering into endless correspondence. There's no time for study or research left.

A short time ago the doctors in France went on a strike and refused to fill out all the reports and keep all the records the politicians asked of them. It took a doctor who was a fast writer a minimum of fourteen minutes to do all the clerical work each patient required. A doctor who took care of twenty office patients in a day had to spend 280 minutes—four hours and forty minutes—doing clerical work.

While socialized medicine has injured medicine in Europe, in America medical science has forged rapidly ahead. Most of the important medical discoveries of the last twenty years have come from America. Today our medicine is far in advance of that in any other country, as doctors of all European countries freely admit, especially in the important field of preventive medicine.

They say that one-third of the people in this country are not adequately fed, clothed or housed, and do not get adequate medical care. The first part is true; but where are the one-third who do not get adequate medical care? In the thirty-four years I have been practicing I have never seen or known of a person wanting medical care who did not get it—and the best that could be given, at that.

Of course there is more sickness among the people who lack proper food, clothing and housing than among the other two-thirds. But the government should see to it that the one-third is properly fed and sheltered before starting in on medicine. No layman or group of laymen know enough about the science of medicine or its practice to pass intelligent laws governing it.

At last Dr. Ferrell arrived, six months after I had expected him. By that time I was completely tired out. I spent a few days showing him about and turning things over to him. Then the charter for the new bank arrived. We completed the organization; I was elected president; and the National Bank opened for business March 9, 1909. I spent the remainder of the day and that night packing, and took the stage for the end of the railroad at daylight the next morning.

With my practice in the hands of a thoroughly competent and reliable man, my business all attended to and my responsibilities ended, it was a grand and glorious feeling when I climbed up to the seat by the driver and waved goodbye.

I spent two nights and a day in Portland attending to a little business for the bank but could not sleep either night. The next afternoon I took the fast train for San Francisco, had a good dinner, and went to bed early. The motion and rumble of the train had a soporific effect, and I slept soundly. My insomnia was broken. I spent two days visiting my parents and then went on to Los Angeles.

To be back among the comforts and luxuries of civilization, away from the ever-present dust of an arid country, and to have plenty of fresh fruit and vegetables and other good things to eat in hotels and dining cars was such a joy that I revelled in every minute of it. With regular meals and plenty of sleep, I gained just twenty-one pounds in twenty-one days, and my hair stopped falling.

From Los Angeles, I went to New Orleans for two days,

then on to Cincinnati, whence to New York, where I visited my oldest brother, who is a civil engineer and was at that time working for the Pennsylvania Railroad in the tunnels they were building under Manhattan. As soon as I was settled in his home on Long Island, I entered the New York Post-Graduate Medical School and Hospital and began work. I spent a month visiting the clinics in nearly all departments, after which I centered my attention on a course in surgery. I worked from 8:30 in the morning until 5 in the evening, and did special work on the cadaver three evenings of the week. The remaining evenings I spent going to shows and hearing good music. It was a wonderful treat after being away from those things more than four years.

There were doctors at the Post-Graduate from all parts of the world, and I was greatly interested in hearing of their work, particularly those doing country practice in the eastern part of the United States, as they worked under conditions very different from those at home.

An old doctor from a little town in upper New York impressed a group of listeners one day by telling of the large territory his country practice covered. He considered sixteen miles a long, hard trip, and was very proud of his driving horse that he declared was good for thirty-five miles any day. His experiences sounded so much like child's play, compared to mine, that I was on the point of telling some of them, when the thought occurred to me that I would not be believed, so I remained silent.

Of course I always drove a team, but thought nothing of going seventy-five or eighty miles a day, or even more, and my regular driving time for thirty-five miles was just three hours and a half. One summer I made three trips a week to a ranch twenty miles from town, and usually rode horseback there and back between 6:30 P.M. and midnight. If I had thought the trip long or hard, I would have taken a team and buggy; I went horseback because I enjoyed the ride.

Two doctors from Wyoming one day listened to an eastern country doctor tell of his hardships, and I could see they were amused. One of the Wyoming doctors then told of some of *his* experiences. They sounded outrageous to the eastern men, but I knew he was telling the truth. After the Wyoming men left the group I remained to hear what might bo said.

"There must be something in the atmosphere of the far West that makes men who breathe it ungodly liars," one doctor remarked. After hearing that remark, I did not tell anyone about the long trips I had had to make.

Sometimes when the grind of frontier practice was hard and the worries and responsibilities great, I had fleeting thoughts of how nice it would be to be a heart specialist in a big city. That idea prompted me to spend all of my spare time in the heart clinic.

One day the professor in charge of the heart clinic directed one of the doctors studying there to listen to an abnormal sound in the heart of a patient. The doctor listened to the heart with his stethoscope but could hear nothing, although he could hear ordinary conversation well enough. The professor sent him to the ear clinic for an examination. The ear specialist could find nothing wrong with his ears and sent him on to the nose clinic. The nose specialist found the doctor had a deflected nasal septum (a deforming curvature of the partition between the nostrils), and operated upon it. From the nose clinic he was sent to the throat clinic, where it was found his tonsils were slightly infected, and they were removed. After having the two operations, and being away a month, he returned to resume his studies. He came in before work started one morning, and all the doctors there were glad to see him back and interested in hearing of his experiences in the various clinics.

When work started he again tried to listen to a patient's heart with his stethoscope but could hear nothing. A look of consternation and dismay spread over his face and work in the clinic stopped. The professor in charge was perplexed. After a few minutes of complete silence, a tall, raw-boned country doctor from western Texas stepped forward.

"Let me see your stethoscope, doctor," he said. As he examined the stethoscope a broad smile spread over his rugged face.

"The bell of this stethoscope is plugged so tightly with lint and debris from your pocket that no one could possibly hear with it," he said. "You could have saved a lot of time by having the stethoscope operated upon instead of your nose and throat."

Everyone but the professor laughed; he only looked a little foolish.

I became acquainted with a young general practitioner from up the state who asked me to go over to Bellevue Hospital with him one day to visit a friend. His friend was an old doctor from a neighboring town who had been in the ward for nervous diseases for several months and had almost recovered from a stroke of apoplexy. While we sat on the vacant bed next to his, talking to him, he complained of having something in his eye. At that mo-

ment, three prominent New York specialists came into the
ward. One of them was a neurologist of world-wide reputation who happened to be in charge of the old doctor's
case.

The old doctor asked the noted specialist if he would
remove the offending foreign body from his eye. The
noted specialist said eye work was a little out of his line
and suggested to one of the men with him that perhaps
he could do it. The second specialist said he knew nothing about the eye and turned to the third specialist. That
noted specialist suggested that they send down to the
eye ward and have someone from there come up and
remove it.

On the impulse of the moment, and without stopping
to think how it might look to the distinguished gentlemen, I stepped up to the old doctor's bed and said, "Let
me see it."

I pulled the lower lid of his eye downward and saw a
little black speck on the inside of it. I took the corner
of my pocket handkerchief and wiped the offending speck
away. The old doctor blinked his eye a few times and
said it felt better. The three noted specialists looked at
each other in silence for a moment and passed on through
the ward without making any comment. After they had
gone the young doctor spoke up.

"There you are, gentlemen; the bigger the specialist,
the more helpless he is when it comes to the common,
everyday things, and the longer he specializes the more
narrow and helpless he becomes. I have had that fact
impressed on me more than ever during the past few
months I have spent over at the Post-Graduate. The more
I watch them operate, the more I am impressed by how

dependent they are on their assistants. If they did not have every facility and convenience, they would be almost helpless. If this craze for specialization is carried too far it is going to ruin medicine."

I began to notice many little things about specialists and specializing that I had not noticed before, and decided I would forget about specializing until I had a good many more years of general practice to my credit. I am not in sympathy with the idea of a young doctor going into a specialty as soon as he leaves college. He should have at least ten years of general practice first; twenty years would be better.

There was so much to be done at the Post-Graduate that was interesting and profitable that I was soon working hard instead of taking a vacation. There was so little responsibility, however, and the work was so easy compared to what I did at home, that it was not tiresome. I had three regular meals a day, if I wanted that many, and plenty of sleep. I enjoyed the novelty of the change for a while, but after a few months the work began to be a little tame and to lack variety and interest. I could not become accustomed to the dead, heavy air of New York, and a world where one could not see more than a few miles through the atmosphere seemed small and cramped. I began to tire of the city with its comforts and luxuries and to long for the dry, rare air of the open spaces where the moonlight sometimes was so bright one could see snow-capped peaks a hundred miles away. I stopped working evenings and went to more shows, but the city was losing its appeal.

A day came when I was fed up with buildings, pavements and crowds of people, and longed for the open country. I went up to The Bronx, to see the zoo, but spent most of the time there looking at the animals from my own part of the country. There were some mule deer and black tail and mountain lions like those at home, but their coats were not so sleek and glossy as the wild ones, and they looked dull and lifeless penned up in cages. There was an old grizzly in the bear pen, looking pensive and woe-begone as he shuffled up to the bars and looked at me quizzically, as though he knew I was from his own country.

The old silver tip stood up on his hind legs and would have talked to me and told me that he too longed for the woods and mountains if I could have understood his language. The sight of him and the other animals in cages, like men in jail, made me a little depressed. I decided that I was really a little homesick, so I closed my work at Post-Graduate in about a week and packed to go home.

I spent a day shopping for instruments and supplies and reserved the last afternoon and night for a final fling along Broadway. When I boarded the Twentieth Century Limited for the West the next afternoon, I felt a bigger thrill than on the morning I climbed up onto the old stagecoach to start East.

On the way home I spent a very interesting and profitable week at the famous Mayo Clinic at Rochester, Minnesota; and a day each in Chicago, St. Paul, Seattle and Portland.

But when I climbed up to the seat by the stage driver on that brilliant July morning, going home, I had the biggest thrill of the whole trip. My lungs filled with the dry rare air tangy with the smell of sage. I looked away to the distant pine-clad foothills and on to the snow-capped peaks of the giant Cascades. The magnificent panorama looked just as I knew it would look and the way it had looked many times before, but it seemed more thrilling than ever. No matter how many times I gazed on that scene, there were always new surprises and new beauties I had not noticed before. The new-born freshness of that wonderful view gave me thrill after thrill, and I realized that while this country remained still so new, fresh and wild, I could never leave it.

Chapter 16

Homestead and Forest

HOME again, brimful of renewed energy and ambition, I was surprised to see that so much progress and development had taken place while I was away. New buildings had gone up and more were under construction. New farm houses were dotting the landscape like mushrooms; wire fences were beginning to form a network. The most exciting news, however, was that engineering crews in the Deschutes Canyon were actually at work surveying for the long-awaited railroad line into central Oregon.

Our new National Bank was growing faster than we had expected it would, with rapidly increasing deposits, and the new cashier was most optimistic for the future.

Dr. Ferrell had done a fine job and won the confidence and respect of all who knew him. Although we had been graduated in medicine the same year, he was several years older than I. He saw service in the Philippines during the Spanish-American War, and was confined in a hospital there nearly a year with tropical fever, an experience which left him much less robust than he had been before. He had a studious mind and a wonderful memory, and he had studied many subjects outside of medicine. He was a very good doctor, an excellent diagnostician, and a big man to place your faith in. We were professionally associated for nine busy and fruitful years, during which

225

time we did an enormous practice without having a contract or written agreement of any kind between us and without the slightest argument or disagreement. He was the most conscientious and unselfish man I have ever known.

At that time Oregon was nearing the peak of its greatest homestead era, with a constant stream of settlers pouring in from all parts of the country. The agriculture experts of the General Land Office in Washington had made a survey of the high desert country and had classified the land as being suitable for dry farming by the approved methods.

The high desert was a vast expanse of level sage brush country, where one could ride fifty or seventy-five miles in any direction from a given point without seeing a house or a fence. Thousands of antelope, mule deer, coyotes, badgers, bob cats, jack rabbits, sage hens, and other animals and birds roamed its wide expanse free and unmolested. Here the stockmen had thousands of wild horses, cattle and sheep running on the open range throughout the year. About a million and a half acres of this land were segregated by the General Land Office and thrown open to entry under homestead law.

The stockmen at once raised a vigorous protest because their range was being taken away, and assured the Land Office that, although the country was excellent stock range, it was entirely unfit for agriculture. The oldest settlers had found it impossible to raise any kind of stock feed there because there was not sufficient moisture. The agriculture experts thought they knew more about it than the stockmen and paid no heed to their warnings and protest.

The real estate men and locators ran out the section lines and were ready and eager to locate settlers on the three-hundred-and-twenty-acre homesteads for a fee of from one to three hundred dollars, and advertised the free land Uncle Sam was giving away far and wide. What if the old settlers did say the country was too arid for agriculture? The experts in Washington knew better. The locators told prospective settlers that any man with from three to five thousand dollars capital who was not afraid of hardship and hard work could make the land support a family by the time the capital was expended.

New settlers flocked in and were captivated by the new country with its abundant wild life, dry rare air and wonderful climate.

Soon two little homestead shacks appeared on each section of the great wide landscape, and wire fences began to mark the homestead boundaries. The timid, curious pronghorn saw his greatest enemy, the white man, appear in ever-increasing numbers in his heretofore peaceful, isolated domain. He heard the terrifying crack of the settler's high-power rifle, as his ranks rapidly thinned and he retreated farther away toward the vast desert expanses of northern Nevada and southeastern Oregon.

Alarmed, wild-eyed and bewildered, the wild range steer sniffed suspiciously at the new scents on the breeze. The wild desert stallion stopped abruptly, snorting his warning of danger to his band of mares, at the new wire fence that shut them off from their favorite water hole.

Wire fences and desert shacks meant little to the sage hens at first. In the mating season the proud sage cock strutted and puffed in front of his coy mate and plopped his enormously inflated air sacks on his ragged breast.

But before the prolific hen had time to hatch her bulging nest of eggs, she often saw the sage brush stripped from the land and her pretty eggs left exposed to view. Before the young birds were fully matured, the homesteaders began shooting them with their shotguns, and they were killed by the thousands to grace the settlers' tables.

Soon squares of dirty brown appeared here and there on the surface of the vast sea of pale green where the settler had cleared his field for the sowing of grain. The grain soon sprouted in the rich lava soil, but as soon as its tender new blades thrust their points above the dry clods, the long-eared jack rabbits swarmed over the fields in thousands and waxed fat on the tasty new fare. In some sections the rabbits ate the grain as fast as it appeared above the ground.

The wily coyote and prowling bob cat found the tame chickens of the settler much easier to prey upon than the wild sage hen that whirred away at their sly approach.

By the time the new settler had purchased a team, wagon and harness, lumber for his shack, wire for his fences to keep the roaming wild stock out of his fields, and supplies for his family, he had made a big hole in his capital, for prices were high so far from the railroad. Then he had to buy feed for his horses and haul his supplies fifty or a hundred miles to get to his land. Water was scarce and was usually hauled several miles by the average homesteader; and if he wanted better firewood than the poor sage brush, he was obliged to cut the scrubby juniper that grew in scattered patches along the rim rock and high ridges. Juniper made a hot blaze and was excellent material for fence posts since it did not rot like other woods, but it was against the law to cut wood of any kind on the public domain. It was the idea of the Land Office that the first crop of settlers, who had the most difficult task in opening up the new country, should not be allowed to use the only available material for firewood and fence posts. It should be conserved for future generations, and their children, and their children's grandchildren— who would have railroads to haul coal to them.

One day a pompous and important individual came into the country and stopped as a guest on one of the large cattle ranches of a prominent cattleman where he was given bounteous hospitality—and no questions asked. This rancher was spending thousands of dollars of his own money hiring hungry settlers to cut juniper for fuel for a dredge, by means of which he was planning to reclaim thousands of acres of rich, marshy bottom-land for farms. The pompous stranger viewed the big operation with great interest, but said nothing, and after a time departed, only to return after several months to have the cattleman arrested on a secret indictment he had obtained in Washington for cutting juniper on the public domain.

The government agent returned to the ranch where he had been an honored guest with a U.S. Marshal, and had the warrant served on the cattleman. After the formalities of the arrest had been attended to, the pompous gentleman asked the ranch cook to prepare a meal for him. The cook reminded him that he had no fuel to cook with except the forbidden juniper, whereupon the pompous gentleman assured the cook that it would be perfectly all right to use the juniper to cook for him, but neither diplomacy nor proffered bribes were of any avail, and the government agent had to ride the ninety miles back to town on an empty stomach.

In due time the rancher went to Washington to face the charge. After much pow-wow with high officials he was told the matter could be compromised and settled out of court if he would pay them twenty-five thousand dollars cash. Much to their disappointment he preferred to stand trial. Many years passed and the government never brought the case to trial, but the important development work was held up. Some of the settlers starved out and left the country; after many more years the cattleman died. The indictment is still on the books in Washington, and the land the public-spirited cattleman attempted to reclaim and make into productive farms is still a river-bottom marsh.

In a few sections where there were not enough rabbits to keep the grain cropped to the ground, it grew rapidly in the fertile lava soil during the spring when there was still a little moisture in the ground. When the hot dry weather came with the approach of summer, it turned yellow and withered before it could head out.

New post offices were established in the homestead country and new towns rapidly sprang up, some with as many as two hundred people. No new doctors came to that part of the country, however. The nearest doctor to me on that side was a hundred and fifty miles away.

The simple life, hard out-of-door work, and wonderful climate made strong men and healthy women, and there was little or no sickness at first. The people were too exhilarated with the fascinating new country and too eager and optimistic for the future to get sick. But with crop failures, lack of proper diet, loss of hope and optimism, sickness began to appear, and it increased as worry and discouragement mounted. Later on I made many long hard trips to the homestead country, usually without pay.

There are always accidents in a new country, however. The first case I had from that part of the country was a man who had been shot with a 45 Colt six-shooter. The bullet struck a big white button on his flannel shirt, directly over the pit of his stomach, was deflected downward and to his right, passed through his right kidney, and lodged in the heavy muscles of his back. He rode ninety miles to town sitting upright in a buckboard, and was still shocked and bleeding when he arrived. After he had rest and treatment for his shock, the bullet was removed, and he recovered in a remarkably short time. He seemed so eager to hurry back to the desert that my curiosity was aroused, and I asked him what was his hurry.

"I wanna git back there an' shoot a button off o' tha shirt of tha — — — that shot tha button off o' mine before he has a chance to change his shirt," he confided.

Failure of the grain crop the first year did not discourage the majority of the settlers; they did not expect much the first year. Failure of their gardens was a more serious handicap as they expected to raise garden truck to live on and expected to can enough for the winter. Many hauled water for several miles for their gardens only to have the frost ruin them. Canned vegetables in the stores were expensive because of the long freight haul from the railroad. The prospect of having to buy canned vegetables at the stores made the settler's remaining capital look much smaller.

The high price of chicken feed that had to be freighted

into the country made it necessary for the chickens to forage at large, and the abundance of coyotes, badgers, skunks, bob cats, eagles, hawks, and owls made chicken raising difficult. Conditions were not favorable for keeping dairy cows, and no hogs were raised as there was no forage for them. Although the antelope were protected by law, they furnished considerable meat to the settlers for a time, but they were soon scarce, very wild, and hard to get. The sage hens were being rapidly killed off. With the appearance of more and more automobiles in the cities, the price of horses began to slump, and some of the hungry settlers occasionally killed an unbranded range horse or colt, but that was still risky. The jack rabbit was the first pest and last resort. Many a jack rabbit was killed for food when provisions were low, although they were not considered fit to eat by most people.

After the second crop failure, some of the wiser settlers began to leave the country. There were many, however, who were determined to stay the necessary five years and prove up on their land, and persisted in trying to make the land produce a crop of grain. When money gave out the head of the family often went to town and got work in order to buy provisions, leaving his family to work on the homestead. Very often the wife and children remained to. plow, grub sage brush, haul wood and water, and do the work of a man.

Upon my return from a long trip to the country late one afternoon, I found a lean, well-tanned, hungry-looking young man from the homestead country waiting for me at the foot of the stairs. He had ridden thirty miles since early morning on an undersized bronco that looked about half fed. He asked me to go and see a woman living on a homestead sixty-five miles from town who had been having a hemorrhage. His cousin, who was her nearest neighbor, had ridden to his place in the night and sent him on after me, while he went back to stay with the woman until I could get there.

She had been left alone, except for a girl of eleven and a boy of eight, while her husband had gone to town to get work. She had been ill several days, but did not allow her neighbor to send for me until her condition became alarming.

I hurried around to see a few patients in town and then started for the homestead, where I arrived just before daylight. I found the woman in a serious condition from the hemorrhage of an incomplete abortion. The blood had soaked clear through the mattress of the bed, and the little girl had placed a tin wash basin under it to keep the blood from dripping on the floor, which was spotlessly clean. There was little furniture in the house but everything was neat, clean, and in perfect order.

The family had sold their little farm in the Middle West and sought a higher, drier climate for the benefit of the wife's hay fever and asthma. They had spent all their money in trying to develop the homestead and the husband had gone to town a month before to get work. His work had not been steady and he had not been able to send them very much money.

Their crops had all been a failure, but they had managed to raise a little garden truck by hauling water six miles, but the frost had killed all of the tender vegetables. For a month they had been living on potatoes, carrots, and dried beans. The woman was thin and so anemic that her blood did not clot properly. They had raised chickens until they ran out of money and could no longer buy feed for them, when the chickens were let out of the pens to forage for themselves. They had eaten what chickens the preying birds and animals of the desert did not get. At that time their only source of food was a general store in a little town consisting of about a dozen unpainted shacks six miles away, where they also got their water.

Although the woman was anaemic, the children looked to be fairly well nourished, and I asked the girl, Alice, if they always had all they wanted to eat.

"Well, I guess me an' Buddy do most always 'cause mamma always makes us eat first," she said. "But I don't think mamma does sometimes, 'cause sometimes there isn't any left." Then she added, "But mamma always says she isn't hungry."

That was about the story of many plucky, self-sacrificing mothers in the homestead country, who often went without food themselves so there would be enough for the children. Too much hard work, without sufficient food of the proper kind, had caused this woman to have a miscarriage.

When the first part of my attention to the woman was finished, and I was about to prepare to inject normal saline solution into her veins, I discovered there was nothing in the house to eat except a few potatoes, and barely enough water to sterilize equipment and make the solution. As it would take me several hours to prepare for and complete the work, I asked Alice if she could do an errand for me.

"Can you hitch up your team and go to the store for provisions and water while I am busy here?" I asked.

Little eight-year-old Buddy straightened up to his full height with a look of superiority and scorn.

"'Course she can, an' I can too," he said proudly.

My team was a little wild, and I was afraid to trust the children with the horses, so I asked them to take their own team and wagon.

I made out a list of provisions that I thought should last the family about two weeks, gave Alice a twenty-dollar gold piece, and told her she must bring everything on the list. She was to tell the storekeeper her mother was sick, but that they would pay whatever balance there might be as soon as her father sent them money.

Her big brown eyes opened wide when she saw the money, and her little brown fist closed on it tightly. She ran to an old trunk and took out a big handkerchief of her father's to wrap the money in, and I tied it around her wrist.

The children hitched the team without help from me; Buddy climbed up on the seat and picked up the lines with all the pride and confidence of an admiral taking command of a battleship, while Alice ran to open the gate. When they passed the neighbor's house, I saw him run out and climb in the wagon with them, and I went on with my work.

In due time they were back from the store with the provisions and water, and Alice set about cooking a meal with all the confidence of an experienced housewife.

By a little after the noon hour I had done all I could for the patient, and after writing directions for Alice to follow for her mother's care, I prepared to leave.

With nourishing food in her stomach and new fluid in her veins, the woman's confidence was restored, and she

took a new lease on life. She made me promise I would
not try to look up her husband in town to tell him of her
illness.

"I'll get along all right now, and I don't want him to
leave his job to come home and take care of me; we need
the money he'll earn far worse than I need him to take
care of me," she said.

The courage and pluck of that little family, fighting a
losing battle against insurmountable difficulties, were inspiring. They were people who would fight to the last,
without complaint, and blame no one if they lost. There
were many others like them in the homestead country,
the sort of people who have formed the foundation and
backbone of our American civilization. Nowhere else have
I seen such exemplification of the brotherhood of man
as I witnessed in the homestead country. Everyone was
always ready and willing to help his neighbor, or anyone whose condition was worse than his own, without expecting any compensation, even if it exhausted his last
resource.

I was often called to see sick homesteaders who needed
proper food more than medicine, and was often out my
time, livery hire, and the money I gave them to buy food.
The majority of them fought to the last ditch, but the
time finally came when they had to surrender and leave
the country.

Many honest, hard-working people lost years of their
time at the hard labor, and all their capital, trying to
make farms out of land that was entirely unsuited for it.
Thousands of acres of the finest range were ruined, for
when the sage brush and bunch grass were cleared off, and
the land plowed, the wind blew enough of the top soil

away so that the bunch grass would not grow again. All because the officials in Washington, who knew nothing about the country, thought it was suitable for dry farming and would not listen to the advice of the old settlers who knew what they were talking about!

One of the saddest spectacles and most costly examples of mismanagement of public lands in Oregon was the ruin of the magnificent pine forests on the eastern slopes of the Cascade Mountains. The slopes and foothills of the Cascades were clothed with a fine forest of ponderosa pine, extending from Canada to the Mexican border.

When I came to eastern Oregon in 1905, all of the beautiful pine timber was an open park-like forest, without any underbrush, where game could be seen for a long distance. Each summer there were many forest fires, the vast majority of which were caused by lightning. As there was no underbrush, these fires consumed nothing but the dead pine needles, cones and twigs that had been blown to the ground by the winds. The little blaze, only a few inches high, crept slowly over the ground and cleaned the floor of the forest of all debris, killing the pine beetles on the ground, but did no damage whatever to the green trees. There were a few dead trees scattered through the forest that had been killed by the pine beetles. These dead trees almost invariably took fire and burned up and the beetles with them. It was these annual fires which had existed for centuries that had produced the beautiful open forests free from dangerous underbrush, and killed so many of the pine beetles that they were held in check. The tiny blaze of these fires was not hot enough to injure the pine seed. When the timber was cut off and the sun was allowed to strike the ground, these little pine seeds began to germinate and a new second growth of trees immediately sprang up.

No one tried to put these annual fires out, as they were known to be a benefit to the timber. When the big lumber companies began to buy the timber, their representatives in the field saw to it that their holdings were burned over every year. If the lightning did not start enough fires, the timber men started more of them.

But when two great railroad systems began their race into central Oregon for the tonnage this timber would afford, the Forestry Department became suddenly Oregon conscious and established new forestry offices and sent in more rangers. These new rangers were fine young fellows, mostly college men, who had acquired their knowledge of forestry from books and knew nothing about local conditions. They all had the same conviction and that was that fire should be kept out of the timber at all times and at all costs. Furthermore, they had orders from the General Land Office in Washington to keep it out, and were equipped with thousands of dollars' worth of fire-fighting equipment.

The experienced timber men on the ground tried to convince them that fire was necessary and beneficial to the Oregon pine, but it was useless. Their answer to all the arguments of the timber men was always the same: "You must keep the fire out of the timber."

Just the same, the men had the timber they owned burned over every year unless they were stopped.

When the fire was kept out of the timber there quickly grew up a thick growth of underbrush, high as a man's head. Then when a fire started it was soon up in the treetops and the raging inferno made so much heat that no one could get near enough to fight it. The fire swept everything before it, burned up the green trees and made the whole area a total loss. The seed in the ground was killed and second growth of trees did not come up, and the ground was soon covered again with a heavy growth of brush.

The land of the lumber companies, which was burned over regularly each year, never suffered loss from fire, and as soon as the timber was cut off a beautiful second growth sprang up immediately.

Not only is the timber under control of the Forestry Department now filled with a heavy growth of underbrush, but it is being rapidly destroyed by the pine beetle. Keeping the annual ground fires out of the timber gave the beetle a splendid chance to increase at an alarming rate. During the past eighteen years the government has spent huge sums fighting the beetle, and is spending more and more each year; but the beetle is thriving as never before. In the *Portland Journal* of April 10, 1936, the following article appeared:

"Salem, April 10. (UP) 'The western pine beetle has killed more Ponderosa Pine in Oregon and Washington in the last five years than fires and the axes and saws of loggers,' State Forester J. W. Ferguson said Thursday: 'Bark beetle claimed 4,507,000,000 board feet of pine in the states of Oregon and Washington from 1931, to 1935, inclusive,' C. S. Martin, forest engineer of the Western Pine Association, wrote Ferguson. 'The loss in Oregon was 3,805,200,000 board feet and in Washington 701,800,000. In the same period the fire loss in the two states has been only 564,585,000 board feet. * * * * * During the past five years the beetles have been killing Ponderosa Pine about three times faster than it has been replaced by growth,' Martin said. 'The beetle damage in timber killed is about eight times that killed by fire. The beetle damage may be from 10 to 100 times the fire loss for any one year. For eighteen years the Ponderosa Pine stands in Oregon, and California, have shown a steady depletion due to bark beetle damage. For the greater part of the commercial stands in Oregon, this depletion has been at the average rate of one per cent a year. No substantial yield of forest production is possible under such conditions.'"

It is hard to predict what the future will be. But it is safe to say that the government will continue to spend millions of dollars every year fighting a losing battle with the pine beetle. The saddest part of the situation is that it is too late to correct the mistake and start burning the floor of the forest each year; the underbrush is now too heavy.

CHAPTER 17

The Doc as Mayor

IT WAS soon known that the surveyors in the Deschutes Canyon were working for the Hill Lines. The Harriman Lines immediately began surveying a railroad line on the opposite side of the river.

For more than a hundred miles of its course, before it joins the mighty Columbia, the Deschutes River runs through the steep, rock-walled Grand Canyon of the Northwest. It is more than a thousand feet deep in most places and furnishes the only gateway through which a railroad may enter the high plateau country of central Oregon from the north. Where the canyon walls rise sheer from the water's edge, the railroad right-of-way had to be blasted from the solid rock. From the brink above the water, where it is not white with foam, it is a crystal-clear emerald green, forming a bright contrast with the rugged canyon walls of warm dark browns, rich reds, and pale fawn, patterned with amazing topsy-turvy formations.

It is a beautiful and inspiring sight to look down upon, but for miles and miles there is not a trail or path leading down into it. Neither was there a trail or road leading up or down the canyon, and the water was too swift and full of falls and rapids to permit the use of boats. Construction gear and tools, supplies for the camps, and even the men themselves had to be lowered over the edge of the canyon wall with ropes in some places.

A spectacular and dramatic battle was waged between the two great railroad systems for the possession of right-of-way at strategic points, for in some places there was room for only one roadbed. Millions of dollars were spent by each road in trying to buy up right-of-way for which they had no other use than to block the other road and keep it out of the coveted territory. Two railroads were finally built, one on each side of the river, but in some places where there was room for only one roadbed, both lines had to use the same track for distances of several miles.

The story was told of a poor homesteader, who, after lonesome, dreary years, had proved up on a homestead, one corner of which extended down into the canyon where it was so narrow and steep that there was room for only one roadbed. Both lines wanted it for the strategic strip of right-of-way it contained, and began negotiating for it. One line finally offered a fabulous price, many times the value of the land, which the homesteader was about to accept, when the purchasing agent of the other road heard of it, increased the offer, and bought the land. The homesteader, who had always been poor, had more money than he knew what to do with and immediately went to town to celebrate.

He took the best room in the hotel, bought the most expensive drinks and cigars at the bar, and left a call for an early hour in the morning so he could tell the clerk to go to hell, he didn't have to get up. Not knowing how to order an expensive meal commensurate with his wealth, he ordered ten dollars' worth of ham and eggs for breakfast. He gave money away, lost some at roulette and faro bank, painted the red-light district a deeper red, and celebrated in every way he could think of. But after a week of celebration he still had money left he did not know how to spend. He then conceived the brilliant idea of buying all the champagne in town, had it poured into a bath tub at the hotel, and took a bath in it—probably the first bath of any kind he had taken in some time.

When it became known that two railroads were headed for central Oregon, the stream of settlers flocking into the country multiplied many times in volume, and the whole country started on the biggest boom in its history. The old horse-drawn stages could carry only a small part of the new settlers flocking in, and automobiles began running from the end of the railroad at Shaniko.

With three other directors of the bank, I organized an auto stage line to operate between Shaniko and Bend. We began with one car, and increased the number as traffic increased until we had seven cars making daily runs. When the travel was at its peak, there were thirty or more cars running out of Shaniko.

When autos began to appear in the country I thought it high time for me to get one, and I bought a Hudson Twenty roadster. With new doctors beginning to locate in the territory I formerly covered, and a great increase in the amount of city practice, I did not make so many country calls as before but still made many long trips.

It was a great satisfaction to start on a long hurry call with a contraption of steel and wheels that could go thirty-five miles an hour uphill and down without tiring. I had expected I would have to give up the sport of shooting rabbits on the road, but as the Hudson had a right-hand drive, I found it easy and convenient to shoot from the seat of the car and continued to carry a six-shooter. Shooting from the car required much quicker work than shooting from the buggy, but that only added to the sport, and I soon became accustomed to it. The auto had some disadvantages, however. It could not be used in parts of the country where the snow was deep in winter and I could not sleep while driving. There was not the same opportunity to enjoy the beautiful scenery, and there was not the chance for thought and meditation that the buggy allowed. I soon began to miss those long night drives over the sleeping desert in the buggy, to sense some subtle change in occult perception or subconscious comprehension that I could not fathom or understand.

The country was changing too. The hand of civilization was destroying the wildness and primitive beauty of the land so much that it began to lose its fascination for me.

Realizing that Bend was beginning its greatest period of growth, the Commercial Club and business men thought it high time to provide for its proper development. Health ordinances were inadequate; there were no sewer systems, no street or sidewalk grades, and no ordinances to govern building construction. The county had gone wet again after a short period of local option that had proved to be very wet in spots, and there was no licensing of saloons.

At a political caucus a ticket for an entire new set of city councilmen was slated, and I was asked to run for mayor at the head of the ticket. I disliked politics and

had neither the time nor inclination to be mayor, but my
name was put on the ticket and I was elected.

My first official act was to issue an order to the city
marshal to stop all gambling in the city.

There were a score or more of applications for a license
to operate a saloon, but no ordinance to provide for the
matter. At the first few meetings of the council there were
heated arguments about licensing. A few prohibitionists
wanted a very high license and no limit on the number of
saloons. They favored dealing the saloon men all the
misery they could because they did not like the business.
I was in accord with the other councilmen who wanted a
small number of saloons with a license moderate enough
to allow the saloon man a fair profit without having to
break the law to make a living. Exasperated by the loss
of so much valuable time and disgusted with the narrow,
deceitful prohibs, I finally announced that the liquor-
license ordinance must be agreed upon at the next council
meeting or I would quit.

I pointed out to the prohibs that the more saloons they
allowed the more open and disorderly the town would be,
and the more time and energy there would be required to
keep it as moral as they would probably want it. Knowing the mayor would be held responsible for the town's
morals, I warned the prohibitionists that if they voted for
more than four saloons I would not waste my time trying
to keep the town moral enough to suit them.

At the next council meeting a compromise was reached
with the prohibs for eight saloons and a yearly license
fee that was far too high. I predicted then that the town
would be plenty open and wild, too much so to suit the

prohibs. And so it proved to be; but I wasted no time and lost no sleep over it.

With the liquor-license question settled, the council got down to business and much was accomplished. A city engineer was employed and street and sidewalk grades were established. I secured the health ordinances of twenty towns and cities in various parts of the United States and studied them carefully. With the collaboration of our very able city attorney, a complete health code was drafted and later accepted by the council.

We got a competent civil engineer to make surveys for a sewer system adequate for a city of a hundred thousand people, one which could be constructed in units as the town grew. The first unit cost over $100,000, and had a disposal plant in the form of an Imhoff Septic Tank located in a natural depression far from the river. Although the overflow from the tank was sterile, it could not get into the river or irrigation ditches.

An adequate code was enacted to regulate building, and the council passed many other ordinances providing for the proper development of the town. But, on the whole, I did not care much for politics. I was far more interested in being the town's doctor than in being its mayor.

CHAPTER 18

Pain and Pretense

WITH the rapid growth of the town, our little hospital was soon too small. Mrs. Hall, who had been in charge of it, left town with her family to return to her former home in Colorado. Dr. Ferrell and I bought a piece of property on the river bank in the center of town, consisting of three lots with a large story-and-a-half house that had been built for a private residence. Remodelled and with steam heat installed, the house was converted into a hospital with a modern laboratory and X-ray equipment. A spacious lawn sloped gently to the edge of a river so crystal-clear that one could plainly see the rocks twenty feet below.

Late one afternoon I received a telegram from the secretary of John F. Stevens, president of the Hill Lines, stating that the contract for the construction of the last hundred miles of the railroad into Bend had been awarded to a contracting firm in Seattle.

Leaving my patients in the care of Dr. Ferrell, I jumped into my car, drove through to The Dalles that night, caught the early morning train for Portland, and was in Seattle by afternoon. I secured a contract with the construction company for Dr. Ferrell and me to furnish medical and hospital care for all their men.

While driving in second gear, about midnight, up the long grade north of Antelope, I overtook a lad of about nineteen walking up the road and gave him a ride. He had lost his job on a ranch and had started to walk and bum his way to Portland in order to save his capital, $10. He was glad to get the ride, but never having been in an auto before, was considerably frightened to be dashing through the darkness so fast. He sat on the edge of the seat, holding onto the dash with one hand and the back of the seat with the other, with one foot out on the running board, prepared to jump if occasion demanded.

When we came to a long stretch of smooth, downhill road, I could not resist the temptation of racing with a jack rabbit that ran straight down the middle of the road in the path of light shed by the headlights. I pressed the accelerator down to the floor board and we went down that long slope as fast as the little roadster could travel. We overtook and passed the rabbit in less than a mile. The lad released his hold on the back of the seat, raised his hand high in the air, brought it down on the back of the seat with a resounding whack, and exclaimed, "Gawd!" Some miles farther on we repeated the performance and he again exclaimed, "Gawd!" That was the only word he uttered during the ride. He was pale and a little shaky when he got out of the car, but very glad to have put so many miles behind him.

Each laborer on the railroad construction work had a dollar per month deducted from his wages for a hospital fee. In each camp along the line we placed a box of first aid supplies, containing dressings, bandages, antiseptics, aspirin, quinine, cathartic pills, cough remedies, medicines for rheumatism, dysentery, and colds, and such remedies as could be dispensed by the timekeeper, as well as liniments and porous plasters for lame backs.

Enormous quantities of porous plasters were being used. On investigation I found that the men were using them to patch overalls, make pads for pick and shovel handles and many other things. Men who objected to paying the dollar hospital fee and did not expect to be sick or injured intended to get their dollar's worth in porous plasters. As the average plaster sold for twenty-five cents in drug stores, these men drew a plaster a week to keep even. After some inquiry, when we found a firm in Boston that sold porous plasters for five dollars a gross, we bought them by the dozen gross and gave the men all they wanted.

Some of the laborers tried to take advantage of the hospital contract in various ways. When they wanted to take a few days off without having to pay for meals, or the weather was bad and they did not want to work, they would pretend to be sick and go to the hospital. If a thorough examination showed no evidence of sickness, the patient was put on a light diet and given an active cathartic. That sort of treatment usually cured the malingerers very quickly and the cure was generally permanent.

One stormy day an Austrian, who thought he was clever enough to beat the game, came to the hospital pretending to be very sick. A thorough examination revealed nothing wrong with him and he was put on the light diet and cathartic treatment. As he made no objection to the treatment, the suspicious hospital attendant watched him closely and soon discovered that he had smuggled a bag of doughnuts, sandwiches, hard-boiled eggs, and a quart of whiskey into the hospital. When he was relieved of his commissary he made a prompt recovery.

At the peak of construction, with about five thousand men in the camps, we were threatened with a typhoid epidemic, when typhoid appeared in some of the camps in the lower end of the Deschutes Canyon. The typhoid was brought to the camps by men who had had it in other places and were still carriers. Once in the camps, it was spread by the flies. But we had a clause in our hospital contract which required the contractors to screen their dining tents, kitchens, and meat houses, and make proper disposal of all sewage and refuse. By making regular trips up and down the line to enforce sanitation, we kept the typhoid in check in the camps, but it began to appear in all the little towns along the line as soon as the construction work reached them. One section of the work was sublet to a young doctor who had just located in a little town on the line. Because of lack of diligence on the part of someone in that sector, he had eleven cases of typhoid at one time in the little hospital he maintained.

With the large amount of rock work and blasting required on nearly every mile of the line, there were many accidents from powder. A dozen men were killed, and twice that number injured in accidental explosions.

The vast majority of the workmen were Austrians and Italians, recently arrived in this country, with Scandinavians and Americans next in order. A striking difference was noted in the ability of the different nationalities to endure pain when injured. The Italians were the most excitable and least able to endure pain, with the Austrians running a close second, while the Scandinavians and Americans stood pain well.

The worst specimen was an Italian who had his little finger crushed with a rock. He became almost hysterical, crying, "Mamma Mia, Mamma Mia," and would hardly allow me to touch the finger to dress it. The finger was so badly crushed it should have been amputated, but he could not be coaxed or forced to take an anaesthetic. After he had remained in the hospital a week without allowing the finger to be treated properly, he was told that he must either have the finger amputated or leave. He packed his grip and started back to Italy, with the finger emitting a very foul odor and fast becoming gangrenous.

On the other hand, the Scandinavians and Americans were not only much more composed at the time of accidents, but they stood pain without complaint when necessary. Sometimes they were even careless and reckless when their own personal safety was involved.

A gang of American steel workers were camped on the north brink of Crooked River Canyon, twenty-six miles north of Bend, where that important tributary of the Deschutes rushes through a canyon nearly four hundred feet deep, and about the same distance across, with perpendicular walls of solid rock. Preparatory to the construction of a railroad bridge, consisting of a single arched span of steel, a heavy steel cable had been strung across the canyon.

One evening at dusk the foreman of the camp telephoned me to come down to the camp and extract the aching tooth of one of his men. I started for the camp at once, but in the meantime the man happened to get a chance to ride to Redmond, six miles up the line, where there was a dentist. He took a few drinks of whiskey, had

the tooth extracted, and after a few more drinks started
to walk back to camp down the railroad right-of-way.
When he arrived at the south brink of the canyon, he had
the choice of crossing on the cable to the camp on the
other side of the canyon or going around by the wagon
road, which would have necessitated his walking four or
five miles farther.

The night was dark, but the fellow was pretty well lit
up by all the drinks he had taken, and he "cooned it,"
hand over hand, across the cable, like a monkey on a
wire. He dropped into the camp a few minutes after I
arrived there and seemed to be entirely oblivious of the
fact that he had taken a foolish and needless risk. If his
grip had given out, or his arms tired, he would have
plunged four hundred feet through the darkness to the
rocks below.

When the bridge was completed, it was three hundred
and twenty feet long and three hundred and forty feet
high, and was at that time the second-highest railroad
bridge in the world.

With the railroads' coming an assured fact and construction well under way, two big lumber companies, the
Shevlin-Hixon and the Brooks-Scanlon, began construction of big saw mills at Bend, with sash-and-door and
box factories in connection with them. All the logs
were to be hauled to the mills on railroads, which would
eventually extend out into the timber for a hundred miles
or more.

The grading and construction work on the railroads
was rapidly pushed to completion with a race between
the two lines; laying of the rails followed quickly after.

In the steel gang that laid the rails into town I noticed

a striking-looking individual known as Shanghai Slim. He was about thirty-five years old, six feet four inches tall, with a magnificent, perfectly proportioned physique, weighing about two hundred and thirty-five pounds. A versatile and much traveled man, he had roamed the face of the earth as a hobo, sailor, prize-fighter, wrestler, steel worker, and what-not, and was about as hard-boiled a roughneck as one could find in a gang of traveling steel workers. He was not a man who would take illness or injury seriously, or be concerned or frightened by it, or be unduly susceptible to mental suggestion or influence. He was the very antithesis of the weak, nervous individual of neurasthenic tendency.

When track-laying was completed and the steel gang left, Slim remained in town and formed a close friendship with a dark-visaged man of swarthy complexion called Blackie, a swamper in one of the saloons.

Late one night Slim accompanied Blackie to the latter's shack on the river bank in the lower end of town, where the two men became embroiled in a drunken argument.

"Get out of my shack or I'll shoot a hole in your hat!" Blackie ordered, reaching for a 25-35 Winchester rifle hanging on the wall, and fired before Slim could rise from his chair. He hit Slim's big ten-gallon hat all right, but the soft-nose bullet went a trifle low, plowed a furrow downward through the scalp, struck the skull, and glanced off through the wall.

At the point where the bullet struck, a round button of bone, a trifle larger than a twenty-five cent piece, was knocked out of the skull and driven under the edge of the intact bone so that it pressed on the brain and caused

Slim to be paralyzed from the waist down. The impact of the bullet did not stun him in the least. On the contrary, it sobered him a little and he attempted to rise from his chair and go after Blackie; but he found he had no use of his legs.

On the following day Dr. Ferrell and I operated to relieve the paralysis. A large flap of scalp was laid back— exposing the area of skull with the hole in it, and the hole was chiseled large enough for the button of bone to be removed.

When Slim got out of bed a week later we found that all of the paralysis had been relieved except in the right foot and ankle. Although Slim seemed to make a determined effort to walk, he had no use of the foot. I felt sure all pressure had been removed from the brain, and insisted that he learn to walk, but he could not get about without two crutches.

After he had been walking around town for three weeks on two crutches, I met him on the street one day and took one of the crutches away, insisting that he learn to use the foot. He seemed unable to do so and secured a cane and went about with one crutch and the cane. A few weeks later I took the other crutch away, but he got another cane and hobbled about with the aid of two canes. After three months had elapsed, with no improvement in the paralysis, we decided to operate again.

Slim had spent the three months loafing in the saloon where Blackie worked, and to atone for the damage his itchy trigger finger had caused, he kept Slim saturated with liquor. He was so toxic from the large amount of alcohol he had consumed that we could not get him completely under the anaesthetic. We tried ether first, but each time he was just ready to reach the stage of complete anaesthesia, his muscles became rigid, his face turned blue, and his breathing stopped. Chloroform did no better. Then we tried a mixture of alcohol, chloroform, and ether, with some better success.

When the flap of scalp was laid back and the surface of the skull was exposed, we found that the hole in the skull where the button of bone had been removed had been filled with a firm, smooth callus, which had not yet had time to calcify. I was just ready to remove the callus and enter the brain cavity when Slim stopped breathing for about the twelfth time. We had serious difficulty in getting his respiration started again that time—for what seemed a very long time I thought he would never breathe again. It was such a close call that we decided to postpone the operation until we could get him in better condition to take an anaesthetic. The scalp was stitched up, his head bandaged, and Slim was put back to bed without knowing that the operation had not been completed. He was soon over the effect of the anaesthetic and wide awake. He had not been told that no pressure had been removed from the brain when a friend came into the hospital to see him.

"Hello there, Jack, I'm all right now, I can move my foot; see!" he exclaimed, as he stuck the paralyzed foot out from under the bed clothes and moved it about with perfect ease. Ten days later he was working with a pick and shovel.

Slim had what is commonly called hysterical paralysis. It was caused by an impression on his subconscious mind that some pressure on his brain still remained after the first operation. As long as the impression remained the paralysis persisted. When his mind was rid of that impression by the second operation, the paralysis immediately vanished. Medical or surgical treatment would not have helped Slim's hysterical paralysis unless it in some way removed the conviction that there was pressure on his brain. On the other hand, if there had been actual pressure on his brain, nothing would have helped the paralysis except removal of the pressure.

I have always been interested in observing and studying the effects of mind and thought on the functions of the human body. An amusing little comedy I witnessed while still a medical student prompted me to take a short course in psychology and suggestive therapeutics soon after graduation.

One summer vacation I took a contract to re-slate the blackboards in a normal school building. For helpers I hired a husky Negro lad about twenty and an uncouth little white man, who was supposed to be a painter. The slating preparation was painted onto the plastering of the walls after the holes and cracks had been filled with plaster of paris and the surface sandpapered. The walls were given successive coats of slating and shellac, and the surface sandpapered between coats, until the blackboard was of sufficient thickness. A large quantity of alcohol was used in the slating mixture, which I mixed myself.

Noting that my alcohol was evaporating rather rapidly and that my helpers were slightly inebriated at times, I spied on them and saw them drinking the alcohol after diluting it with water. While eating lunch in a restaurant at noon that day, I formed a plan to check the rapid evaporation. The little pseudo-painter went home for his noonday meal while the colored boy brought his lunch in a dinner-pail.

The darky had eaten his lunch and was asleep under a shade tree on the campus when I returned. There was a museum on the top floor of the building, with many mounted animals and birds, and a collection of snakes, frogs, bats, and small reptiles, preserved in glass jars of alcohol.

Selecting a glass jar of about a gallon size, with a big black snake in it, I carried it down on the campus where the Negro boy was taking his after-dinner nap. Poking his ribs with my foot to waken him, I asked to borrow his pocket knife.

"Yaas'er," he said, as he reached into his overalls without looking up. When he handed it up to me he spied the jar with the snake in it, and his eyes bulged so that the whites loomed large.

"What's you-all gwine ter do wid dat dere jaa?" he asked suspiciously, as I began loosening the rubber washer under the lid with the knife blade.

"Well, Henry," I said confidentially, "if you'll promise to keep it under your hat, I'll tell you. I'm going to take some alcohol out of this jar to use in the slating mixture. I've taken all I dared to out of the other snake jars, and this jar has more in it than it needs anyhow."

By that time things began to happen and Henry got mighty sick. He soon lost all of his dinner and seemed to be trying to bring up some of his internal decorations.

"You must have eaten something in your dinner that has given you ptomaine poisoning," I said, trying to look serious.

"Oh Gawd, I'se shoo pizened all right, boss, u-u-ur-rup,

I'se shoo pizened, I'se shoo gwine die, oh mammy, mammy, I'se pizened," he moaned.

About that time the little painter returned from his lunch and came over to us. Eyeing the jar of alcohol with the big snake in it suspiciously, he asked what was the matter with the colored boy. I told him I thought he had ptomaine poisoning from something he had just eaten. On the pretext of going after a cup of water for the sick boy, I left the two helpers there alone for a short time, as I knew the badly frightened boy would tell the painter that they had been drinking alcohol from the jars with snakes in them. When I returned with the water, the painter was sitting on the grass deathly pale and mopping his brow with his red bandanna.

The Negro wanted to get home where his mammy could care for him and he could die in his own home surroundings. The pseudo-painter thought it would be a splendid idea for him to take the sick boy home, so I told him to go ahead and return to work as soon as he could. He did not show up on the job until the following morning, and the darky did not return until the next day. From that time on the alcohol did not evaporate so rapidly.

The alcohol my helpers had been drinking was the best grade of grain alcohol I could buy at the drug store and had never been near any snakes. It was the suggestion that he had been drinking alcohol from the snake jars that made him sick, not the alcohol. I doubt very much if the alcohol from the snake jars would have made him as sick, had he taken it unwittingly, as the thought of it did.

Psychological manifestations such as these two cases present are the result of the workings of definite, immutable laws. There is nothing supernatural about these laws, unless all universal law is to be considered supernatural. While medical treatment has no effect on imaginary illness, neither does mental or psychical treatment have any effect on genuine illness of actual pathology. But hope, freedom from fear and worry, and confidence in the doctor will aid in the treatment of both real and imaginary ills.

Many times I have heard of marvellous cures being made by mental faith or religious healing methods in cases of real illness where there was actual pathology, but I have never been able to find an authentic case, although I have searched diligently. On the other hand, many, many people have lost their lives from real disease by using different forms of faith and religious healing, when they could have been cured by medical or surgical measures.

Early in my practice I had such a case. A middle-aged woman consulted me because of pain and distress in her abdomen, and I found she had an abdominal tumor which could have been easily removed by a surgical operation. She was afraid of an operation, however, and her relatives and friends persuaded her to take a religious cure. She soon came to the point where she insisted the tumor had been taken away, although it continued to grow larger to the extent that she had to let out her skirt bands. Even after it grew so large that she was unable to walk, she insisted it had been taken away, but it finally killed her. I have known of many similar cases, and I can assure the reader that there is no form of mental, religious, or faith healing that ever did or ever will cure a tumor of any kind.

CHAPTER 19

The Golden Spike

THE spectacular race between the two great railroad systems of Hill and Harriman to gain the coveted central Oregon country ended when the rails reached Bend. On October 5, 1911, the golden spike was driven home by James J. Hill of the Great Northern road with appropriate ceremonies. The celebration that followed was a kind of wake over the demise of the last great frontier. It marked the beginning of a new era in the saga of the vast country of forest and desert, the central Oregon country I knew and loved. The frontier had been pushed back a hundred and sixty miles south from the Columbia River.

Along with the railroad, the automobile arrived to hurry up the tempo of life, to push the faithful horse still farther back into the remoter regions. Great saw mills would soon begin eating away the beautiful pine timber, and the bright green blanket of forested areas would shortly be stripped to expose ugly brown barren hills, cut and scarred by canyons, disfigured and sullen.

New people of various types and cultures from all parts of the land came flocking into the country to mingle with the old pioneers, stockmen and buckaroos. They came from small towns and farms and big cities back east. They came from Europe. They came from machines

260

in factories, from shops and stores, from offices surrounded with bustling clerks and stenographers, singing to the tune of rattling typewriters. They came from everywhere.

Soon I had so much city practice that I had no time for long trips into the country. When I did go I whizzed along in an auto with all my attention centered on driving. I no longer had the hardships; but neither did I have the opportunities to think and dream or the time to marvel at the wonders of the star-studded canopy over the sleeping desert.

I found I missed the old days—and nights. Somehow, they had afforded surcease amid the swiftly moving kaleidoscope of events and the frenzied behavior of men and women.

Man and the world at large were so different from the preconceived ideas and notions I had formed from early teachings that I was sometimes confused and bewildered. Both in sickness and in health man is a paradoxical creature, defying reason, logic and science, so bewildering as to cause mind to wonder if our sciences will ever be able to wrest his secrets from him.

My constant surprise, after I began to practice, was the layman's ignorance of doctors and medicine and his relationship with them. For example:

When long country calls began to come frequently, I soon noticed that they generally came about bedtime. By evening the sick person was tired, more nervous, restless and apprehensive; and so were his friends and relatives.

One of the first country calls before the railroad came

from a ranch thirty-five miles out. About nine P.M. the telephone rang:

"Hello, Doc, this is John — out at the — ranch. Say, Doc, my boy's been sick all day. I want you to come here right away."

I got there at about one-thirty A.M. and found little Johnny had been sick three days. The father and mother had been putting off calling me—although they had called once while I was away. An hour and a half later I had finished my attentions to Johnny, my team had had a rest and a feed, and I prepared to start back to town.

"Why, Doc, you aint goin' to start back home at this time a night. Stay here an' git a little sleep an' hev some breakfast with us," they urged.

"Thanks, I'd like to but I must get back to town," I said. "I'll have just about time enough to get there, get a shave and a breakfast in time to go to work."

"Oh! Is there somebody sick in town, Doc? Is it anybody we know?" the rancher asked in surprise.

"Yes, there are several people sick in town, John," I replied.

"Well, my! Is there an epidemic there, Doc? What's the trouble? Maybe I'd better not let my wife and kids go to town; do you think it's catching?"

You see, John hadn't thought it possible that anyone else could be sick at the same time as his Johnny.

The doctor's greatest problem is the innocence or ignorance of the patient, the lack of cooperation. But my persistent endeavors bore a little fruit. People out there in that lonely country actually did begin to call their Doc earlier; prospective mothers did learn that they should have advice during the period of gestation; men came to understand that if they didn't want to become cripples (as so many of the old-timers were) they'd better see the Doc. There was such a thing as progress.

During the years that have sped by and wrought so many changes since the golden spike was driven home, the healing art has passed through its greatest and most rapid period of development. Public opinion is far behind, but the public is learning too, and rapidly.

Will medicine ever be able to learn all the secrets of health, disease and reproduction? So much has been learned and so much more remains to be discovered! But just so long as the doctor remains a free agent to study, investigate, experiment and practice according to his own conscience and the conscience of the great historical body of medical ethics, medicine will march forward.

My work as a young medico was bound up with the lives and emotions and creeds of Americans of all kinds —including the original Americans, the Indians, the old-time Yankees and Southerners, the new immigrants from every part of the world. To the doctor a man is a man, and a woman is a woman, and a child is a child. He's conditioned that way by his training. He has to be impersonal or go nuts, as they say today. It's the medicos alone, it seems to me, who see their fellow-men, not as masses or concepts, but as mortals, susceptible to the ills that flesh is heir to.

When I watched the ceremony which marked the beginning of a new era and the close of an older one, I felt a mingled emotion; there were both triumph and regret. The old frontier went with the golden spike. And I had been a part of it, at the same time influential to a modest degree in ending it. But it's written into my life forever.

6 · C65°5A